FLEXING YOUR SOUL

MOVING WITH ENERGY AND CONSCIOUSNESS

Energetic Movements and Exercises
to Energize and Integrate Body, Heart, Mind and Soul

Jalieh Juliet Milani & Alessandra Shepard, Ph.D.

Pathwork Press
Charlottesville, VA
2005

PRINTED IN CHINA ON RECYCLED PAPER
11 10 09 08 07 06 05 10 9 8 7 6 5 4 3 2 1

Library of Congress Cataloging-in-Publication Data

Milani, Jalieh Juliet, 1971-
  Flexing your soul : moving with energy and consciousness / Jalieh Juliet
Milani & Alessandra Shepard.
     p. cm.
  Includes bibliographical references.
  ISBN-10: 1-931589-10-0 (alk. paper)
  ISBN-13: 978-1-931589-10-9
  1. Stretching exercises. 2. Vitality. 3. Chakras. I. Shepard,
Alessandra, 1936- II. Title.
  RA781.63.M54 2005
  613.7'1--dc22
                       2005008251

Text design: Gastao Guedes
Cover Font design: Gastao Guedes
Front Cover design: Gastao Guedes and Jalieh Milani
Back Cover design and production: Lisa Willow
Text photos used by permission: Gastao Guedes
Models: Andrea Castro Jota Teixeira, Celia Isabel Rodrigues, Eduardo Luiz Davidoff Chagas Cruz, Gustavo Alejandro Rodriguez, Mariella Bondezan Afonso Rodriguez, Vera Dutra.

Dedication

To John Pierrakos, founder and proponent of Core Energetics as a transformative process that integrates the body, feelings, mind, will and spirit through the purposeful directing of consciousness, I dedicate the following pages. It was through his pioneering, intense and inspiring spirit that these Energizing Movements became an experience to me.

To Siegmar Gerken, for being present and grounding his own gift of creativity, for artistically and intuitively guiding me toward my first steps on the path of awakening my body to my heart's call and my mind's awareness.

To my parents, Paul and Alessandra, who have been a source of inspiration as sincere and devoted seekers on the path of self-discovery and self-revelation, I dedicate the following pages. Through their tireless and continuous search and sharing, I was introduced to John Pierrakos at one of his workshops as a birthday gift.

To Connie Zakos, who through her generosity of spirit, kindness of heart and delightfulness of being, made it possible for me to begin my journey toward the Core by opening her home and her heart so that I could pursue the Core Energetics training.

To my daughter Allegra and son Daniel Badi, both of whom through their smiles and movements manifest the joy and life-fulfilling experience of embodiment as they, step by step, choice by choice, awaken and direct their energy and consciousness toward and into spirithood.

To my husband, Peiman, who has encouraged me silently and patiently as a steadfast supporter of my being as it experiments, expands and contracts, and as we daily choose to share and tread the path of discovery and revelation of self and other.

To our Creator, I am eternally indebted and grateful for bestowing consciousness upon this human form and a deep longing to search, become, love and serve as I seek to traverse His numerous worlds….

Jalieh

I dedicate this work to Raymond Paul Shepard, my life partner. Together, we have been traversing the many worlds of God forever, and I am grateful.

To my parents, Sara and Irv, for their patience and love.

My children, Warren, Erica, Andrea, Eloy Ramin and Jalieh Juliet, you are children of light and I love, honor and respect you. It has been both a joy and a challenge to participate in your lives.

It is with the deepest gratitude that I also dedicate this book to John and Eva Pierrakos; John for developing Core Energetics and for being my teacher, and Eva for bringing forth the Pathwork, the spiritual and psychological foundation for this work.

Alessandra

Table of Contents

Preface

Our body is the vessel for the physical experience of our Being. It enables us to touch, feel, exchange, explore and create on a physical level. For this reason we give great value and care to our bodies in terms of health, exercising, appearance and so on. However, we also may lose ourselves in reducing life to physical existence, forgetting that this vessel is also the carrier for our emotional life, mental capacity and a channel through which our essence unfolds.

In an open system, all these qualities of life flow into one stream that expresses itself in a movement that I call the pulsation of Being (see exercise on page 63, The Pulsation of Your Being). That includes all our life functions from metabolic processing and emotional responses. Our capacity to think, experience, integrate and direct is based on this natural pulsation of our being.

Nevertheless, from birth to adulthood, we have to deal with intrusions into our openness. Depending on the outer circumstances and our internal capacity to meet them, we develop protective mechanisms like slowing down or holding our breath, contracting muscles, numbing nerves, or others which result in the reduction of our feelings and awareness. Ultimately, this limits our perception of reality, the unfolding of our consciousness and of our lives. All this restricts the free flow of life energy and leads to stagnant places in the human body and energy system. In my present research with physicists and medical practitioners, we can now objectively document this by infrared diagnostics, photon emissions and other scientific measurements.

Life is expressed by its pulsation. Pulsation is movement. Change is defined by movement, so the more we allow the conscious movement on all of our levels of existence, the more we not only feel good, express ourselves in creative ways, but also allow the expansion of our consciousness and soul movement.

To support people in sustaining and expanding their physical, mental, emotional and spiritual integrity, Jalieh Milani and Alessandra Shepard have written a most comprehensive and holistic exercise book. The authors have experienced and studied these exercises in our trainings first hand. As practitioners and teachers, they developed and refined their approach so that, with their professional experience and artistic capacities, they wrote *Flexing Your Soul* to address the whole person.

Jalieh Milani and Alessandra Shepard write with a deep commitment to further the well-being of their clients and humankind in general—with warmth, knowledge and integrity. Moreover, *Flexing Your Soul* is unique in calling attention to what is being experienced in the moment energetically and emotionally. It is like following a piece of thread to see where it might lead us, knowing that each experience is unique and depends on how we respond to each movement. The value of this work lies in its ability to awaken us a little more. As we awaken, consciousness expands, and with that, so does our individual power to impact and contribute to our lives and others.

I know this book will find its way into the hands of many body-oriented and holistic practitioners and to people interested in enhancing their lives. With these exercises, we increase our potential to activate the flow of energies, reconnect with our essence, allow the will of the heart and move toward the greater unification of our being.

Siegmar Gerken, Ph.D.
Director, Institute of Core Energetics
Worldwide Trainings
Mendocino, California

Introduction

Flexing Your Soul—Moving with Energy and Consciousness is a practical manual of Energetic Movements for your entire body and your entire being. The movements and experiences presented in this manual are based on a very specific premise about the nature of human reality. That is, that the soul, human consciousness, is the inseparable, immutable essence of who we are. The soul comes first, along with consciousness. When the soul unites with the body, they embrace and become one. The seed of our physical reality is our consciousness. Our bodies, ideas, beliefs and emotions are the living sculptures of our life experiences. They form and shape themselves according to the way we learn to survive and live, in our family, community and world.

The purpose of these exercises is to help us reach and sustain a more authentic and fulfilling life. This is done through the direct experience of the open and flowing energy in our body with our thoughts and feelings. As this integration becomes increasingly possible, we can reach a state whereby:

what I believe,

what I think and

what I feel,

are aligned

and reflected

in what I do and experience

and thus,

in who I am

here and now.

Through the steadfast practice of the Energetic Movements presented here, you will increasingly activate your energy and consciousness and bring about a greater internal coherence and integration of your body, emotions, mind and spirit. You will improve your ability to sustain and share a life full of joy and love.

The exercises in this manual may be used individually in support of self-directed exploration and development, or for deeper work and exploration with a body therapist, such as a Core Energetic Therapist. See more information in the section in this manual titled **What Is Core Energetics?**

This manual is unique for it focuses on exercises that elicit a sense of being present in the NOW with our energy. It asks that the one performing the movements consider connecting with their feelings and emotions, as well as to be willing to gently question closely held ideas and beliefs. This is not emphasized in most exercise programs. Most exercise programs have an entirely different focus, emphasizing the rhythmic and increasingly automatic repetition of movements. To be present in one's body every moment while doing most other exercises is not necessary. Thus, the movements become automatic. When we do the exercises in this manual with consciousness, we are opening a door so that something new can happen. We are bringing awareness into our bodies. In this case, our body is matter. We are incarnating in a deeper sense when we do the exercises. We are *present* in the moment—we are connecting with our feelings and experiencing the movements in our bodies. Our mind is connected to what is happening with our bodies. We are more than we were. We actually feel and look more alive. We are spiritualizing matter.

We say this because so many times when we are with people, we see their blank stares, a state often referred to as fantasy or daydreaming. The person is not fully present. If we think of our bodies as our home, we would say that much of the time no one is at home. We are not present. Few of us are immune from this daydreaming, including when we drive our cars, go shopping, or when we are with others in simple social interactions, even in important and vital decision-making moments.

The exercises in this manual are for everyone, but were particularly designed for people who are either awakening to new possibilities for themselves or have already discovered the value of this personal work and want to continue to heal and become even more whole. This includes many body therapists, teachers, trainers or individuals who know from personal experience the importance of body work in their lives.

Core Energetics means getting back to basics: like breathing, moving, feeling our feelings and being able to express these feelings. Part of us would like to be able to do this, but there is another part of us that resists. That part is often unconscious, it is saying: "NO." Some of the ways that we resist are by tightening our muscles, slowing down our breathing, sometimes to a stop. In doing the exercises and movements in this manual, your awareness will increase and you can learn more about your resistance.

Additionally, these exercises can be used by professionals to increase energy and awareness with therapy clients before sitting down to talk, doing some other activity, or sometime during the session. These exercises are also useful in groups before starting a meeting, and even in the middle of meetings, when we sense people are not paying attention and the group energy is low. The coffee and doughnut break, the more traditional way of bringing the energy back to a group, no longer has the appeal that it used to have for many of us. Doing a few of these exercises is a healthier and more effective way to help people get energized and focused on the task at hand, plus, they are not diabetes or calorie producing.

We are sure that you can find many creative uses for these exercises. Try them for several weeks and see how you too can begin to feel a difference.

The Purpose of the Energetic Movements

The purpose of these movements is to encourage and foster *grounding, expansion and integration*. That is, to make more energy available to be directed toward purposeful and aligned action of the entire body, heart, mind and spirit—of the human being as a whole and, with that, raise our level of consciousness. For this to take place, one needs to energize and distribute the energy throughout the body. There are places in our bodies that are BUBBLING with energy, others that are "no-man's-land," where we tend not to even notice them in our day to day. And there are those parts of our body which we feel are continuously depleted, tired, and weak. This varies from person to person as to the location of the main areas of energy depletion and energy concentration in the body. With these Energetic Movements, you will be able to experience energy flowing more fluidly in your body.

Energy Anatomy and Chakras

As we move our physical body, so are we moving our energetic body. For those of you who have an interest or even curiosity about energy anatomy and the human energy field, each Energetic Movement has an outline of a body illustrating the chakras that are being activated when the Energetic Movement is performed. You will find additional information that explains the chakra system, how it functions and its relevance and importance to the quality of our life and to our overall health, in the section at the end of the manual entitled **Energy Anatomy**.

Energetic Movement Benefits

- The Energetic Movements enable you to achieve greater flexibility, freedom to move and express, muscle tone and overall body fluidity.

- Following the movements in a systematic manner, you will gradually gain more awareness and release some of the blocks that freeze up your body, thus not allowing you to fully experience its gracefulness and strength. In this way, by practicing these movements consciously, you will begin to feel more alive and free up more of your potential as a more fully integrated person.

- Over time, as you continue experiencing the Energetic Movements, and as you slowly let go of internal resistances, you will experience the positive benefit of getting more in touch with your emotions, thereby increasing the quality of your life.

- Practicing these movements, you will begin to tread your own pathway of growth by thinking and acting with more authenticity and presence, because you will be in touch with the truth of your own being.

Tips on How to Use This Manual

How This Manual Is Structured

Flexing Your Soul—Moving with Energy and Consciousness is a practical, hands-on manual that invites **YOU** to experiment with and experience over 80 Energetic Movements for your entire body & being.

The Energetic Movements are divided into eight segments, one segment for each part of the body and a ninth segment of Energetic Movements that unify and harmonize the body as a whole. The nine Energetic Movement segments are:

For each of the segments and their corresponding Energetic Movements, you will find the Instructions on how to perform the Movement, illustrative photographs and an Energy and Consciousness description. This description includes the chakras that are primarily being activated with the particular movement being performed, as well as their relevance regarding your health. The consciousness part elicits awareness of your experience in the moment. When you read this section in each exercise, we invite you to slow down and become aware of your feelings at that moment. Ask yourself: How is my energy? What am I aware of now, inside? Further study on the subject can be followed by looking up the topic in the suggested list of readings in **Bibliography and Further Readings**.

Most of the Energetic Movements can be performed individually; however we have included **20 exercises** that can be done in **pairs** and in **groups** if you choose to use them that way. The exercises for pairs and groups work best with a facilitator who has had experience with groups and particularly in the area of body psychotherapy. The exercises are rich in possibilities for exploration and offer you the possibility of greater health on all levels as well as increased self-awareness. Our experience has shown us that there are some things that we all have in common no matter what our age, culture or background, and other things that are unique to each group, and of course each person. This makes the pair and group exercises an exciting forum for learning about yourself and others.

We have also included an **Individual Sample Program** at the end of this book. The Individual Sample Program is a suggestion of a possible sequence of exercises that you may choose to follow as you become familiarized with the exercises. We have suggested a sample of movements that energize the eight segments of your body and a ninth segment for the body as a whole. You can mix and match Energetic Movements as you would like. As you explore your body and self through the movements, you may give preference to a certain segment of the body at one time and another segment at another. In time we hope you will explore and experience each and every one of the over 80 movements offered here!

If you would like to contact either one of us, you can find our information in the section **About the Authors**. We look forward to your feedback about the Energetic Movements and how they have touched you—body and soul.

On Taking Full Advantage of the Energetic Movements

We would like to offer you a few suggestions to keep in mind and body while performing the Movements with Energy and Consciousness.

Know Thy Self

- With any physical activity, we must begin from where we are. That is, you know what you can do and how far you can stretch comfortably so that you can finish an exercise and continue with your daily activities. If you need to consult a medical specialist before engaging in any or certain types of physical activities, we recommend you do so before initiating the movements included in this book.

- Throughout the 80 plus Energetic Movements many of them will invite you to move, stretch and tense and hold your body in positions that you have not been used to. We invite you to begin every new exercise slowly, taking into account what is right for you at the moment, such as the number of repetitions for each one of the exercises.

- Start slow and increase the speed and intensity of the Movement as you feel you are able to.

- You can mix and match the Energetic Movements to fit according to your needs or the needs of those you are assisting.

- As you perform the Movements, pay attention to how your body is reacting, how you are feeling and your thoughts.

- We encourage you to begin experimenting with your own physical and mental limits. When you feel ready ask yourself: *"How much deeper can I go with this stretch or with this breath? How much more fierceness or lovingness can I express with my facial expressions or my touch?"* When you reach the place in you or in your body that says *"I cannot go any further"* you will most likely have reached what we call **The Saturation Point.**

• **The Saturation Point** is a state in us that signals to us that we have reached a personal limit at this particular time. Notice what are your physical, emotional and mental *Saturation Points*. When and where do you feel you cannot go any further; when you say "No way, Jose"? Gradually challenge your physical, emotional, and mental *Saturation Points* as you repeat the exercises and in your daily life. With time and dedication, our present limits will expand and new horizons will open up and be experienced.

Breathing

• Breathing is an essential function of and for life. The breath is a source of nourishment to our bodies, muscles, tissues and organs. Our breath sustains life. It also sustains our emotions. If we do not want to feel, we unconsciously hold our breath. Or if we want to keep things superficial, we tend to breathe only with our upper chest, not allowing the breath to fully draw into our bodies and reach our bellies. When we allow ourselves to fully experience the breath, we make our bodies, emotions and minds fully available to life, with everything it has to offer us, including pain and pleasure. Consequently, for us to mobilize more of who we are and be more fully alive, we must begin to consciously experience our breath.

• Throughout the Energetic Movements, you will be encouraged to allow for your breathing to continuously flow through your nose naturally. Any other method of breathing associated with an exercise, such as holding your breath or exhaling through your mouth, will be clearly indicated in the movement instructions.

• **The Breath Path**. In certain exercises you will be invited to breathe by inhaling through the nose and allowing the inhalation of the air to start by filling your belly, diaphragm, and going up filling your chest and lower throat. You will then exhale through your mouth, by releasing the air from your lower throat, chest, diaphragm and lastly from your belly. This is what we call *The Breath Path*. Try it a couple of times right now. How does it feel? Begin to notice whether you are breathing following *The Breath Path* or whether you are skipping some part. Continue practicing and soon it will become a natural, beneficial and enlivening experience for you.

Emotions @ Work

• Emotions are really e-motions, that is, energy in motion. For every thought, every action, there is an emotion connected to it, even if the e-motion is one of indifference. Thus in the Energetic Movements, e-motions are ever-present as we move our bodies in a purposeful manner.

• The Energetic Movements will elicit all kinds of emotions in us, from more subtle and soft to more explicit, assertive, and even outright aggressive. We invite you to experience and experiment with the range of emotional currents that you have in you and the power that they have to season and often take over your experiences and life. Ask yourself as you explore the movements *"What emotions am I more comfortable with? Which ones would I rather not have or not even show? What would happen if I were to show them?*

What would I feel then"? You will see that when we consciously engage our emotions it is a workout in and of itself!

- Over time, as we follow the Energetic Movements and slowly let go of our resistance, we will experience the positive benefit of getting more in touch with our emotions and tap into their power to color and bring growth experiences into and expand our lives.

Your Voice

- The inclusion of the voice in the Energetic Movements, when indicated, is of the utmost importance. Your voice carries with it the energy as well as the intention that you give to the movement. Voice adds a dimension of depth and grounding, inviting you to be fully present in body, mind, and emotional expression.

- In certain Energetic Movements, you will be invited to let out a resounding "Ha" or a sighing "Ha" as you exhale. In the beginning it may feel strange to *"make noise"* while breathing, since most of us try to breathe and live unnoticed, *"minding our own business."* Yet the discomfort we may feel could be a clue that we do not easily assert ourselves and could likely profit from some work with our emotions. In this way, we will gradually own our own sound bites!

- Through the Energetic Movements our softness and our assertiveness will reveal themselves more fully. We will notice that our bodies relax more when we include our voice. As we try to relax naturally, our sighing comes forth. So let us begin de-stressing our lives by exhaling with a natural and soft "Ha," a sigh of relief pleasurably given. Our bodies, minds and hearts will thank us.

Where Do I Begin?

You may choose to start with the suggested **Individual Sample Program** that can be found at the back of this book. We recommend that you look through and read the Energetic Movements before you begin. This way you will be able to follow the sequence and focus your mind and emotions on what the exercise is requesting of you. Moreover, you will be able to take greater advantage of the *Energy & Consciousness* dimension of the exercise, since you will know what the relevance of that particular exercise is for your life. Do keep in mind our suggestions *On Taking Full Advantage of the Energetic Movements* as you perform each and every exercise. Feel enjoyment as you move your body, heart, mind and soul toward a more fulfilling, pleasurable and authentic life!

ENERGETIC MOVEMENTS

The following Energetic Movements are for specific segments of the body. All of the exercises in some way directly or indirectly help us to ground. Because grounding is basic to who we are, and where we are, we would like to make a few comments about this important concept in the field of body work. When we are grounded, we are in conscious contact with the earth that supports us. We might feel that this Earth is our real, our true mother, and that She receives us with open arms. We are in the now. We are present to the flow of our energy, and we can choose to use it in our life or we can let it dissipate in our distortions and lose it. We can feel our power in the lower half of our body or numb it out and remain in our head as is most common in the Western world. Many of us are aware of such expressions as "plant your feet on the ground." It means: "Get solid and know what is going on." Grounding, like the tree spreading its roots for stability, is a physical act. Grounding is also an emotional act, with mental and spiritual components. An emotionally grounded child, meaning a child who has a close loving relationship with parents and family, when learning to walk will soon feel safe and will not hesitate to spread the roots of her consciousness and explore his new world. Mentally, grounding has to do with knowing where we stand around some issue or idea. Being spiritually grounded means having a connection to Spirit, to the Divine, or to God. The following movements and exercises were designed to enable you to experience becoming more of who you were intended to be here and now.

1. Feet & Ankles

The following exercises were designed to strengthen our grounding. When we are grounded, we are like a tree connected to our basic source of energy. When we are ungrounded, we can feel rootless, we do not feel secure. The grounding stance is most useful to open the first chakra and connect with our vitality. It also helps in keeping us present and in the moment. Grounding enables us to be present, here and now. When we listen to our body sending us this simple message, our life begins to change. Being grounded is fundamental. We stand upright, feel connected and sense that we can take care of and support ourselves. We can say, "I am here" with surety in our voice. Try doing the grounding exercises while saying out loud, "I am here." How does that feel? If it feels true, you know it. If it does not feel true, you also know it. Where are you when you are not here?

INITIAL GROUNDING STANCE
THE BOW
JUMPING JACK FLASH
CROSS-COUNTRY SKIING
ANKLE CIRCLES
WEIGHT SHIFT
TOE STRETCH
TOE FLEXING
WEIGHT SHIFT WITH BOW
FOOT MASSAGE WITH A TENNIS BALL

3

1 Stand with feet shoulder-width apart. Feet are parallel to each other. Knees are slightly bent. Hips are comfortably supported by legs. Abdomen is relaxed, as is the rest of the upper body. Face is naturally facing forward.

4 As the *tempo/speed* of the raising and releasing of the heels to the floor increases, so do the "Ha" sounds coming from your belly, up and out of your mouth.

2 Slowly raise both heels, yet maintain knees slightly bent. As heels are raised, breathe in. As heels are released and stomp the floor, breathe out, while letting out a "Ha" sound that comes from the abdominal area.

5 This is a continuous rhythmic movement. Place hands on hips for greater balance and stability.

6 Do this energetic movement for a few seconds the first time and gradually work up to minutes at a time, allowing for personal stamina and ability to increase.

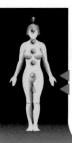

3 Little by little, increase the speed of the movement.

Energy & Consciousness *This Energetic Movement encourages us to become aware of our stance and how we distribute our weight on our feet. It assists us to guide our body to a more harmonious body posture by bringing our consciousness into the standing position. We become aware of the strength of our legs, and the steadiness and safety in keeping our feet on the ground and supporting the rest of our body. Our breathing will also become steadier. Overall, this movement energizes our entire body, beginning with the first and second chakras, starting from the feet and up toward the head.*

1 Stand with feet shoulder-width apart. Feet are parallel to each other. Knees are slightly bent. Hips are being comfortably supported by legs. The abdomen is relaxed, as is the rest of the upper body. The head is naturally facing forward. Arms are relaxed on either side of the body.

2 Keep chin parallel to ground. Eyes looking forward.

3 Slowly bend upper torso backward. Arms are parallel to each other, raised to the side of the head by the side of the ears. Palms are facing each other, fingers relaxed.

4 Breathe naturally from the belly.

5 Hold in this position as long as possible. Notice if there is any trembling, sweating or resistance. Continue to breathe naturally.

6 Release the bow position by moving the upper body forward and relaxing it until hands approach or reach the ground.

7 Breathe deeply and allow back and leg muscles to elongate.

8 Slowly move upward, vertebrae by vertebrae.

9 Return to initial standing position.

10 Note: For greater back support and a deeper stretch, instead of raising the arms to either side of the head, place hands in fists on lower back while allowing for a deeper arch back.

Energy & Consciousness *We can feel a certain tension as we hold our body in an unfamiliar position. In the beginning, it might feel like a strain for us. As we practice a number of times, we can move into this position more readily, and this will help open the second, third and forth chakras. These chakras especially have to do with the flow of energy into our feeling centers. Because of this, it is possible to experience some fear or resistance. When we do body work and go into our resistance, we can even begin to feel a slight amount of nausea. If that happens to you, ask yourself: "What am I resisting in my life?" Over time, as we continue doing these exercises, our awareness expands. As we let go of our resistance, we can relax and allow more sweetness into our lives.*

1 Begin by freely, joyously jumping up and down.

3 Now jump up once, twice, thrice, and on the fourth time, open arms wide and release a deep "Ha" sound as you are suspended in the air in the cross-like position, arms spread out away from chest, parallel to the ground.

2 Continue jumping up and down, but now bend further down on the knees and then jump up, as high as possible, toward the ceiling.

4 Repeat 5 or 6 times.

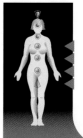

Energy & Consciousness *This jumping exercise will help open your second and third chakras. Opening your arms wide while releasing a sound opens the fourth chakra. The front chakras that are being activated have to do with our feeling center. Working in this way may stir up some feelings. If that happens, put your hand on your body where the feeling comes from. It's all right to acknowledge feelings and allow the feelings to emerge. Notice what you want to do with the feelings once you become aware of them.*

1 Focus your attention on your standing position. Feel your feet on the ground. Breathe naturally.

2 Set RIGHT foot forward. Feel entire foot sole on ground, preferably on a carpet or soft surface.

3 LEFT foot remains firmly planted on the floor, assisting with your balance.

4 Slowly move RIGHT foot in such a way that the entire sole of the foot does not loose contact with the ground. Slide the RIGHT foot back and forth a few times, feeling the sole of the foot warming up, waking up.

5 Include arms, as if imitating a walking motion, for better balance while performing this movement.

6 Switch to LEFT foot.

7 Repeat movement.

8 Now stand on both feet. How does that feel? Any different?

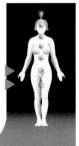

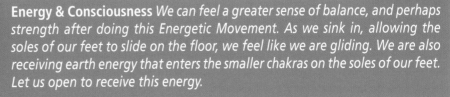

Energy & Consciousness *We can feel a greater sense of balance, and perhaps strength after doing this Energetic Movement. As we sink in, allowing the soles of our feet to slide on the floor, we feel like we are gliding. We are also receiving earth energy that enters the smaller chakras on the soles of our feet. Let us open to receive this energy.*

1 Stand with feet shoulder-width apart. Feet are parallel to each other. Knees are slightly bent. Hips are being comfortably supported by legs. Abdomen is relaxed, as is the rest of the upper body. Face is naturally facing forward. Notice body and weight distribution on feet.

6 Repeat a couple of times.

7 Switch to the LEFT foot and repeat both the clockwise and counterclockwise rotations.

8 Return to standing position.

2 Gently lift RIGHT heel so that only the ball of your foot and toes are in contact with the ground.

3 Keeping your weight on the toes of your RIGHT foot, slowly rotate right ankle in a clockwise direction.

9 Breathe deeply. Bring attention to the weight distribution on your feet.

4 Repeat a couple of times.

5 Change to a counterclockwise rotation.

Energy & Consciousness *How does it feel to stand with your feet on the ground now? You probably feel a greater sense of stability. Are you more balanced? Notice how your feet are supporting you. How does that feel? By activating the ankle joints with this movement, this enables the energy to flow more easily through the joints.*

1 In a standing position, notice your body and weight distribution on your feet.

3 Return to standing on both feet. Notice any difference in standing stance.

4 Now shift weight to inner sole of RIGHT foot. Breathe.

2 Starting with RIGHT foot. Shift entire body weight onto the outer side of RIGHT foot. Breathe. You are literally standing on the side of your RIGHT foot.

5 Return to standing on both feet. Notice any difference in standing stance.

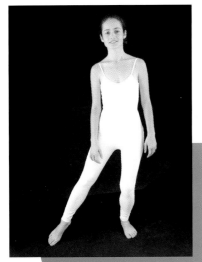

6 Repeat to LEFT outer and inner sole.

Energy & Consciousness *This movement assists you to begin getting grounded. Energetically, part of being grounded means that the first and second chakras are open. You can begin to feel good about your body as well as experience a connection to your vitality that helps make life more exciting. This movement helps to begin to activate the first and second chakras.*

1 While in a kneeling position, flex feet and sit on toes.

4 The upper body can remain erect or you can choose to bend backward increasing the pressure on your feet, by placing more of your body weight on them.

2 Breathe as toes, specially big toe, are stretched forward.

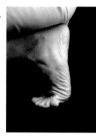

5 If the stretch is too intense, use arms to decrease the amount of pressure on the toes, by gradually lifting the body's weight from over the feet.

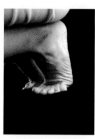

3 Adjust body weight forward or backward according to the desired depth and intensity of stretch.

6 To exit the stretch, place hands in front of knees on the ground and slowly raise body to standing position.

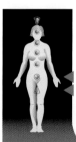

Energy & Consciousness *Putting our weight on all of our toes to stretch them feels good. Very often our toes are bunched together like bananas in shoes that are stylish and pointy. Toes are the part of our feet that are the most flexible. Toes help to stabilize us. How do you feel when you are unstable?*

1 Stand *barefooted*, preferably on grass, carpet or rug.

2 Feet are parallel to each other. Knees are slightly bent. Hips are being comfortably supported by legs. Abdomen is relaxed, as is the rest of the upper body. Face is naturally facing forward.

3 Breathe naturally.

4 Feel the soles of your feet in contact with the ground. How connected and aware are you of your feet and the ground?

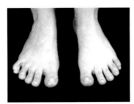

5 Grasp with toes at the ground, both feet simultaneously.

6 Grasp as if seeking to pick something up or make holes in the ground.

7 Notice the strength your toes.

8 Now stand on both feet. How does that feel? Any difference?

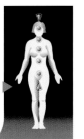

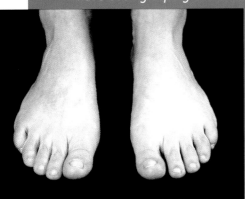

Energy & Consciousness *The purpose of this movement is to energize and increase contact with your toes. Look at your toes and see how they are shaped. If they are curled under, perhaps they have been grasping at the earth or floor for a long time? This can be a movement in search for stability or just trying to hang on when you were a child. If you feel that you are still doing this, what might you be hanging on to now? We have a tenth chakra. It is below our feet, about a foot and a half below the ground. It is the first to be formed. If the 10th chakra isn't functioning well, you may experience being ungrounded or dizzy and confused about what you are doing here, and what your life's purpose is. If you are not grounded, you may experience an inability to deal with stress or cope with everyday realities. This chakra holds daily life energy, nurturing and substance.*

1 Begin in a standing position

2 Shift body weight to slightly bent RIGHT leg.

3 Place LEFT leg to the side of your body while keeping it straight so to assist you maintaining balance.

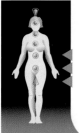

4 Keep the big toe of your LEFT foot barely touching the ground for stability.

5 Upper body is arched, with arms at waist. For a greater back stretch, place fists on lower back.

6 Maintain your natural rhythmic breathing pattern while holding this position.

7 Hold until *The Saturation Point* is reached.

8 Return back to the initial standing position.

9 Breathe and feel your stance.

10 Shift body weight to the LEFT leg and repeat the movements above described to the LEFT side.

11 Breathe naturally throughout the movement.

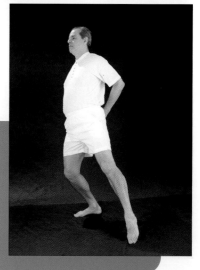

Energy & Consciousness *The above movement is a little more advanced than the previous movement. For the more adventurous, when you return to the initial standing position, make sure your knees are slightly bent. Can you elicit a slight vibration from your legs? See if this vibration, which builds slowly, can be felt throughout the lower portion of your body. This helps the overall energy system to flow. It can also generate a sense of pleasure in your body.*

1 Standing Position. Knees are slightly bent. Hips are being comfortably supported by legs. Abdomen is relaxed, as is the rest of the upper body.

2 Place tennis ball at the center of the RIGHT foot. Keep balance by placing body weight on LEFT leg.

3 Slowly roll RIGHT foot over ball.

4 Breathe.

5 Increase pressure downward on ball, to increase the foot massage as you roll the ball with foot, ensuring that the ball makes contact with every part of the sole of your foot: from toes to heel, including the sides of the foot.

6 Switch to the LEFT foot.

7 Repeat the same movements with the LEFT foot.

8 Return to standing on both feet. Notice any difference in standing stance.

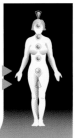

Energy & Consciousness *The soles of our feet have a vast amount of nerve endings. Reflexology, the art and science of pressing on certain points on the soles of our feet, often brings relief and healing. A Reflexologist can pinpoint areas on the bottom of the feet where there are nerve endings for the colon, diaphragm, the spine and, actually, our entire body. Therefore, massaging with the tennis ball can also bring general relief from stress or even a headache if you find the right spot to massage. This movement can remind us that we have smaller chakras on the bottom of our feet and that we can receive earth energy whenever we choose to.*

13

2. Thighs & Legs

For this segment, our attention will be focused on the lower part of our body. As with the ankles and feet, our thighs and legs support us in an upright position. If we feel supported by our feet and legs, we will have a sense that we can take care of ourselves. When we are uptight, or stressed, our knees tighten up and block the energy that is flowing to feed and nourish our body. These exercises, done consciously, will strengthen and increase the flow of energy in the lower half of your body. They will also add strength to your desire to stand firm when that is important to you, as well as your desire to back off when that is appropriate.

THE ELEVATOR
THE TRIANGLE
SITTING TRIANGLE STRETCH
OVERALL WARM-UP
MULE KICKBACK
KNEE WARM-UP
BODY DRUM
KICK FORWARD, KICK SIDEWAYS

1 Start in standing position. Gradually bend into a squatting position, where thighs are parallel to floor, *as if you were sitting on an imaginary chair.*

2 Once the imaginary sitting position is reached, slowly move upward into standing position.

3 Keep a continuous up and down movement. Start faster and then go slower.

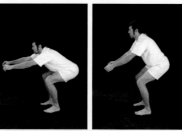

4 Now stop and hold in the sitting, 90-degree position until you reach *The Saturation Point.*

5 Slowly rise.

6 Work up to 5 or 6 repetitions of this movement.

7 To stretch and release accumulated tension after this movement is completed, stand upright and gently kick legs forward, one leg at a time, loosening the thigh, hamstrings and calf.

8 Note: This exercise can be done standing against the wall. Breathe continuously and hold until *The Saturation Point*. Make sure that when you are sitting in the imaginary chair, you are able to see your toes at all times. Ensure that your knees do not overcome your toes. For this not to occur, it is suggested that you keep your weight on your *heels* and are able to see your toes at all times throughout the exercise.

Energy & Consciousness *This movement energizes the first, second and third back chakras, and the first and second front chakras, by opening, stretching and holding your thighs, pelvis and lower back in a challenging position. Many enjoy this challenge. Some of us don't. In either case, try it. We might want to voice our complaint while doing this by making sounds or just saying out loud: "I don't like this." Or make a fist and shake it while doing the movement. Our back chakras are related to our will center. We will need our will to do this movement. Although this movement will strengthen your thighs and pelvic area, it may also create intense stress. With the continuous repetition of this movement, your thighs will get stronger, and it will slowly release the tension you may have accumulated in your lower back.*

1 Open legs as wide as comfortably possible into a triangle. Lower upper body forward, along with hands, to the ground. Walk with hands forward, keeping soles of feet at all times fully planted on the ground. Feel hamstrings stretch.

2 Continue to breathe naturally.

3 Remain in the forward stretch as long as you can. For a deeper stretch, press your chest down in the direction of your knees.

4 Slowly move hands toward feet and then gradually bring feet closer together.

5 With slightly bent knees, move upper body, vertebrae by vertebrae, to the full standing position.

6 Note: For a further stretch to legs and lower back, one can, while bent forward with hands on the ground, raise one leg and kick it back, while letting out a "Ha" sound with the kick. Kick a few times and then switch legs. Hands remain on the ground, supporting the body in that position, while the head is looking forward or toward the ground.

Energy & Consciousness *Our calves are one of the areas of our body where we hold our emotions, especially feelings of wanting to control situations and other people. Therefore, the calves concentrate a lot of emotional tension. We encourage you to rub your calves and even make fists with both of your hands and gently pound your calves while bent forward in the triangle position. The hands in fists gently pounding is often used in shiatsu massage. With this, we are sending a message to our body to wake up and surrender.*

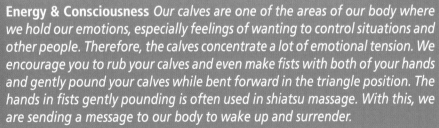

1 Choose a partner and face each other.

2 Sit on floor, with legs as wide apart as possible. Both partners' feet are touching.

3 Partners reach with outstretched arms for the other partner's hands.

4 Hands hold tightly.

5 Slowly one partner starts to pull the other partner toward him. The partner being pulled slowly bends forward, seeking to touch his chest on the floor between his legs.

6 Breathe.

7 The partner being pulled will let the other partner know when to stop pulling him forward. When the partner being pulled asks to stop, the stretching stops. The partner being pulled remains in the stretching position breathing as naturally as possible. Then slowly the partner being pulled will go back to his initial sitting position.

8 Switch partner being pulled into the stretch.

9 Repeat stretch 2 or 3 times with each partner.

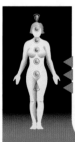

10 To exit the stretch, gently bring legs together and shake them against the floor. Slowly return to a standing position. Kindly assist your partner to stand, if necessary.

Energy & Consciousness *This stretching movement energizes the first, second and third chakras. It will open the blocks in the thigh and pelvic area, releasing the accumulated tension. This is another way to ground you and to receive energy from the earth while having fun!*

1 Stand with feet shoulder-width apart. Feet are parallel to each other. Knees are slightly bent. Hips are comfortably supported by legs. The abdomen is relaxed as is the rest of the upper body. The face is naturally facing forward. Arms are relaxed on either side of the body.

2 Breathe in deeply and exhale with a "Ha" sound 3 or 4 times.

3 Raise RIGHT knee toward the chest and then switch, raising LEFT knee toward the chest.

4 Increase tempo of knee raising so that one is jumping, knees alternating to reach chest.

5 Include the hands. Hands hit knees as knees alternately rise to meet hands.

6 Start at a slow speed, then increase, going as fast as possible, then gradually decrease the speed of raising the knees.

7 Stand erect with both feet on ground. Take 3 or 4 deep breaths.

8 Bend at the waist, hands reaching toward the ground. Knees are slightly bent.

9 Allow for the breath to become steadier, the back to relax and elongate.

10 Breathe deeply and allow back and leg muscles to elongate.

11 Slowly move upward, vertebrae by vertebrae.

12 Feel your body as you stand erect.

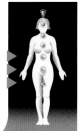

Energy & Consciousness *This Energizing Movement stimulates the first, second, and third chakras. It will open the blocks in the thigh and pelvic area, releasing the accumulated tension while activating the energy in the legs. Do you now feel more prepared to work on these exercises? Or, perhaps, are you ready to go out and meet another kind of a challenge?*

1 Place yourself on all fours.

2 Head is facing forward or downward.

3 Kick back with LEFT leg.

4 As you kick back with your heel, let out a "Ha" sound and exhale.

7 Alternate between LEFT and RIGHT leg several times.

5 Inhale as you draw the LEFT leg back to initial position.

6 Switch and repeat to RIGHT leg.

8 Note: For a greater stretch, straighten the knee that is on the floor supporting your body. Now kick back, as you let out a resounding "Ha" with every back kick. Then alternate legs.

Energy & Consciousness *This is fun and it also feels good. We are opening our first and second chakras. That means more vitality. The second chakra also has to do with our sexuality. Whatever we are holding on to, we can let go of in this movement. What words do you want to speak while doing the movement? Sometimes I say, "Out" or "Get out." Energetically, we are pushing out from the back chakras. This involves our will center. We use our will to control, perhaps because we are afraid of not being in control or allowing ourselves to be vulnerable. The mule kick can also help us to release the frustration at the end of a difficult day. Maybe there is something you have in mind that you would like to energetically kick out of your life? Try it by doing this exercise.*

1 Stand with feet close together for greater balance. Hips are comfortably supported by legs. Abdomen is relaxed, as is the rest of the upper body. Face is naturally relaxed.

2 Slightly bend knees as to imitate a sitting position. The back is erect.

3 Rest both palms on knees.

4 Gently rotate knees clockwise as if drawing an imaginary circle with the knee movement.

5 Pause.

6 Switch to gently rotate knees counterclockwise.

7 Repeat 3 times in each direction.

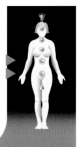

8 Return to standing position.

Energy & Consciousness *Our knees are most important. Without our knees we would not be able to stand upright or be able to bend down. Many people have problems with their knees. Indeed, one of the most common surgeries being done today is knee replacement. Exercising our knees will help keep them healthy, particularly if we are not extremely overweight. In addition, if you would like to experience energy healing, you can rub your hands together until they begin to warm up, and put them on your knees for some gentle healing when they are tired.*

1 Stand with feet spread apart at a comfortable distance. Feet are parallel to each other. Knees are slightly bent. Hips are being comfortably supported by legs. The abdomen is relaxed, as is the rest of the upper body. The head is naturally facing forward. Arms are relaxed on either side of the body.

2 Raise both heels from the ground simultaneously, keeping knees slightly bent.

3 As the heels are off the ground, raise arms to chest height, with open palms facing down, parallel to the ground.

4 As the heels are raised off the ground, the palms move up, while parallel to the ground. As heels drop forcefully to the ground, the palms press downward, as if pushing the energy from the palms to the ground.

5 This is a continuous up and down movement of both heels and palms.

6 Initiate this movement slowly and gradually increase the tempo and intensity of pushing down against the ground with palms as well as pressing down with heels.

7 Softly transition to decrease the tempo until it is very slow.

8 Let out a "Ha" sound every time the heels stomp the ground, while maintaining the eyes wide open.

9 Return to the standing position and feel your entire body vibrate, the breathing expand in your chest. You are present, here and now!

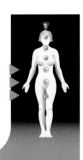

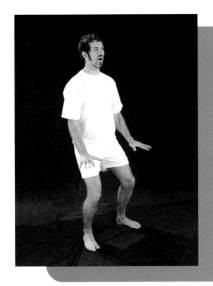

Energy & Consciousness *This movement energizes the entire body, by rhythmically activating the legs and arms. After you have experienced this movement, you will feel wide awake, present, energized and ready to fulfill your heart's desire. You will begin to experience the well of energy and possibilities that are within you ready to be called upon. This grounding stance is most useful to open the first chakra and connect with your vitality. It is powerful, as it helps in keeping you present and in the moment. By including the directed and forceful movement of the hands and arms, this movement strengthens the awareness and importance of the energy moving from the upper part of the body toward the ground. This will assist the energy to be grounded, which will make it more available for you to direct to an area of your choice in your life.*

1 Stand with feet shoulder-width apart. Feet are parallel to each other. Knees are slightly bent. Hips are being comfortably supported by legs. The abdomen is relaxed, as is the rest of the upper body. The head is naturally facing forward. Arms are relaxed on either side of the body.

2 Imagine that you are at the seashore, feet in the water, enjoying a beautiful sunny day. Playfully and gently kick RIGHT leg forward a couple of times.

3 Then, in a jovial and fun manner, kick RIGHT leg to the RIGHT side. Experiment kicking at different angles and heights.

4 Switch to LEFT leg and repeat the movements done on the RIGHT side.

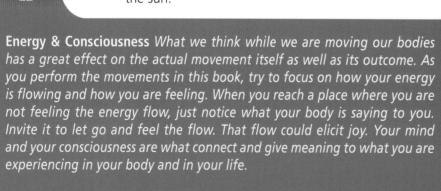

5 Return to standing position with a joyful smile and enjoy the sun.

Energy & Consciousness *What we think while we are moving our bodies has a great effect on the actual movement itself as well as its outcome. As you perform the movements in this book, try to focus on how your energy is flowing and how you are feeling. When you reach a place where you are not feeling the energy flow, just notice what your body is saying to you. Invite it to let go and feel the flow. That flow could elicit joy. Your mind and your consciousness are what connect and give meaning to what you are experiencing in your body and in your life.*

3. Pelvis & Abdomen

Is your pelvis strong and healthy? The pelvis supports the entire upper body. Anatomically the genitals are in the pelvis. This is a place of pleasure or pain, and for some of us, both pleasure and pain. For some the pelvis is a place that is so painful that the pain has numbed the area, so that it goes unnoticed. Our abdomen also holds feelings and various strong emotions like anger and depression. We can learn to access those feelings. Becoming aware of our feelings is a first step toward healing. These exercises will help you to begin, or to continue, on the path of self-discovery.

GROIN WARM-UP
SQUATTING
LEG LUNGE
HIP THRUST
STANDING PELVIC THRUST
THE BUTT MASSAGE
THE FROG
PELVIC THRUST LAYING DOWN
WAIST WARM-UP
BELLY MASSAGE

1 Note: Move gently into this exercise, since the muscles in this area are not usually exercised.

2 Stand with feet spread apart at a comfortable distance. Feet are parallel to each other. Knees are slightly bent. Hips are being comfortably supported by legs. The abdomen is relaxed, as is the rest of the upper body. The head is naturally facing forward. Arms are relaxed on either side of the body.

5 You may choose to keep at least one hand on RIGHT knee to direct the knee in the completion of the full circle.

6 Change the direction of the RIGHT knee rotation.

7 Alternate directions a few times.

8 Repeat with LEFT bent leg.

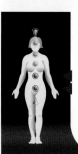

3 Start with raising the RIGHT bent leg as close as possible to your chest.

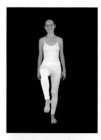

4 Rotate the RIGHT bent leg to the side, outward, then moving toward the back and then toward the front, completing a full circle.

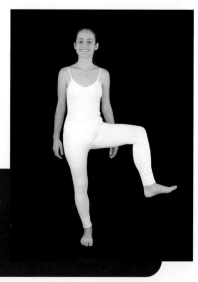

Energy & Consciousness *This movement opens our second and also affects the third chakra. Here we are working with the quality of the expression of our creativity and sexuality. Energetically, this also reflects on how much we are committed to taking care of ourselves and our health.*

1 Stand with feet spread apart at a comfortable distance. Feet are parallel to each other. Knees are slightly bent. Hips are being comfortably supported by legs. The abdomen is relaxed, as is the rest of the upper body. The head is naturally facing forward. Arms are relaxed on either side of the body.

2 Face your partner and look in to each other's eyes.

3 Extend your hands so that you and your partner are holding hands.

4 Slowly squat while keeping your and partner's balance.

5 Breathe.

6 Go up and down a few times, experimenting with balance, difficulty levels and intensity of squatting stretch.

7 Stand up slowly and kick legs forward to release accumulated tension in thighs.

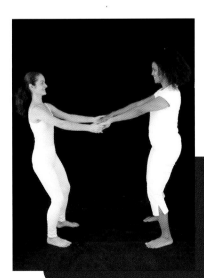

Energy & Consciousness *We are working with the first and second chakras. Do you think that you would like to squat down by yourself or with your partner? Try it both ways and see how it feels to support yourself or to support each other. Do you enjoy giving and receiving support? Or do you prefer to just take care of yourself? This is for the purpose of your awareness.*

1 Stand with feet shoulder-width apart. Feet are parallel to each other. Knees are slightly bent. Hips are being comfortably supported by legs. The abdomen is relaxed, as is the rest of the upper body. The head is naturally facing forward. Arms are relaxed on either side of the body. Breathe naturally.

2 Place RIGHT leg as far forward as possible. Slowly bend RIGHT leg while LEFT leg remains straight behind the body. Feel the stretch in the groin area. Place hands in front of body, on either side of the RIGHT leg for greater support and a deeper stretch.

3 Slide the LEFT back leg as far as possible from the RIGHT leg for an even deeper stretch.

4 Breathe normally throughout the stretch.

5 Slowly come back to the initial standing position.

6 Shake the RIGHT and LEFT legs.

7 Repeat the same sequence, but his time with the LEFT leg being placed as far forward as possible.

8 Repeat with each leg 2 or 3 times.

9 Variation: This same sequence can be done placing the RIGHT leg as far to the RIGHT side as possible, thus lunging sideways. Repeat with the LEFT leg and lunge as far to the left.

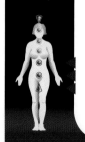

Energy & Consciousness *How far can you lunge forward and still keep your balance? I challenge myself every time I do this exercise. Risk stepping further, and then see if you are still in balance. Do your legs feel strong and capable of supporting you in this position? Or is it a struggle to hold yourself up? If it is a struggle, how do you respond to this struggle? Do you try harder or say to yourself, "I can't do this"?*

1 Stand with feet spread apart at a comfortable distance. Feet are parallel to each other. Knees are slightly bent. Hips are being comfortably supported by legs. The abdomen is relaxed, as is the rest of the upper body. The head is naturally facing forward. Arms are relaxed on either side of the body.

2 Gently move the hip to the RIGHT side, then FORWARD, to the LEFT, then to the BACK.

3 Gradually increase the tempo/speed of this hip movement to all four sides in a counterclockwise direction.

4 Begin to energetic and purposefully thrust the energy coming from your hip to the RIGHT, FORWARD, LEFT and BACK. Imagine you are trying to throw the energy of your hip to someone standing in each of the four sides you are thrusting.

5 With each thrust, let out a resounding "Ha" sound.

6 Keep breathing naturally.

7 You may choose to experiment moving clockwise as well as randomly as you thrust the hip.

8 Decrease the tempo of the thrusting, so that it becomes one *fluid circling* of the hip and waist in a clockwise direction.

9 Switch to a counterclockwise direction, slowing even more the circling of the hip and waist until you reach a standing position.

10 Stand, breathing and noticing the wave like sensations in your pelvic area.

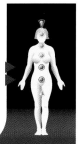

Energy & Consciousness *This movement stimulates the opening of the second chakra and moves the pelvis. It will help to loosen up the tension that one usually holds in the area as well as allow a greater fluidity in the sacrum and thus mobility in the spine. This movement encourages the freeing up of the well of creativity, passion and self-assuredness for our relationships and for our life.*

1 Stand with feet spread apart at a comfortable distance, wider than shoulder-width apart. Feet are parallel to each other. Knees are slightly bent. Hips are being comfortably supported by legs. The abdomen is relaxed, as is the rest of the upper body. The head is naturally facing forward. Arms are relaxed on either side of the body. Breathe naturally.

2 With the knees slightly bent, slowly move pelvis forward and backward in a wave-like motion.

3 Include arms to assist in the balance and intensity of the thrust.

4 Increase the intensity of the forward thrust.

5 As the pelvis moves forward, the arms go back at waist level.

6 At the forward thrust, exhale and let out a "Ha" sound.

7 As the pelvis moves backward, consciously arch the back, and inhale.

8 Start slowly and increase the speed and intensity of the thrust as you feel you are able to.

9 Slowly return, continuing the wave-like motion with the pelvis, to the standing position.

10 Keep your knees slightly bent and notice, while you are breathing naturally with your eyes closed, if there is a vibration or waves flowing throughout your body.

11 Remain standing and enjoy the life that is moving within you.

12 Variation: Instead of a forward thrust, make it a backward thrust movement. Thus, as the buttocks thrust backward let out a "Ha" sound. Remember, you can modify the intensity of the thrust in any direction.

13 Variation: This movement can be done in pairs or groups. In either case, make sure the pairs are close enough, but not too close so that their forward thrusts will not cause either one of them to hit the other. In addition, ascertain that each person in the pair is looking into his or her partner's eyes as they thrust forward. After the pairs are done invite them to share with each other what their feelings and thoughts were during the exercise.

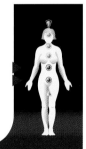

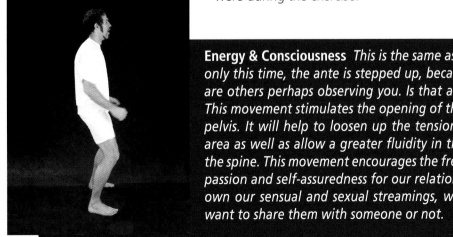

Energy & Consciousness *This is the same as for the individual pelvic thrust, only this time, the ante is stepped up, because you have a partner or there are others perhaps observing you. Is that alright or, do you feel inhibited? This movement stimulates the opening of the second chakra and moves the pelvis. It will help to loosen up the tension that one usually holds in that area as well as allow a greater fluidity in the sacrum and more mobility in the spine. This movement encourages the freeing up of the well of creativity, passion and self-assuredness for our relationships and for our life. Once we own our sensual and sexual streamings, we can then choose whether we want to share them with someone or not.*

1 Sit with your knees bent, legs comfortably apart and feet on the ground.

2 Head is facing forward.

3 Breathe deeply 3 times, letting out a "Ha" sound on the exhalation.

4 Place your hands on or underneath your knees, lifting your feet off the ground.

5 Sway your back to the back so that you are maintaining your balance by being on your buttocks.

6 Now begin to move, directing your knees in a circular motion.

7 This motion is as if you were rolling on your sitting bones.

8 Move very slowly so that you can feel the buttock's sore areas.

9 Breathe a few times every time you reach a sore area and relax while in that position.

10 Note: You can place your hands to the sides or behind you on the floor to assist you in keeping your balance and for greater support.

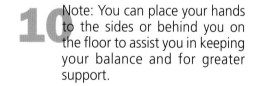
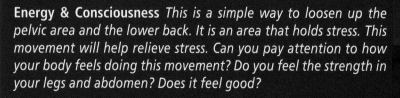

Energy & Consciousness *This is a simple way to loosen up the pelvic area and the lower back. It is an area that holds stress. This movement will help relieve stress. Can you pay attention to how your body feels doing this movement? Do you feel the strength in your legs and abdomen? Does it feel good?*

1 Stand with feet spread apart at a comfortable distance, wider then shoulder-width apart. Feet are parallel to each other. Knees are slightly bent. Hips are being comfortably supported by legs. The abdomen is relaxed, as is the rest of the upper body. The head is naturally facing forward. Arms are relaxed on either side of the body. Breathe naturally.

4 Bounce buttocks, back and forth, up and down, stretching the inner thighs and back.

2 Slowly move downward into a squatting position.

3 Place hands in between legs, in front of you for balance.

5 To intensify the movement, jump up and down on feet keeping the same position.

6 If you feel adventurous, bounce around the room in the squatting position.

7 Note: Notice if your heels are able to remain flat on the ground when you are in the squatting position or if they come up from the floor automatically. Try to keep them on the floor, that way increasing the contact with the ground as well as intensifying the back of the lower leg stretch.

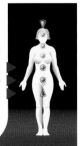

feels good. It is opening up the flow of energy, and it might bring us back to some of the freer moments of our childhood. Pay attention to your face during this movement. Is there a smile, or are you doing this with a straight face? Having fun is good for our health. Allow your inner child a chance to come out and play.

1 Use a mat to support back and buttocks

2 Lying down on back. Knees are bent; feet are parallel to each other on the ground, spread apart at a comfortable distance, wider than shoulder-width apart. Lower back is touching the ground. The pelvis is slightly tilted forward. The abdomen is relaxed, as is the rest of the upper body. The head is naturally looking toward the ceiling. Neck is relaxed. Arms are relaxed and placed on either side of the body. Breathe naturally.

3 Thrust pelvis upward, so that the lower back is off the mat.

4 With the upward thrust, exhale and let out a "Ha" sound.

5 Start slowly and increase the speed and intensity as you feel you are able to. The back of your arms and upper shoulders will support you as you thrust upward.

6 Increase the intensity of the upward thrust.

7 As the pelvis moves upward, tighten the buttocks and arch your back to increase the pressure upward.

8 Hold the upward thrust a brief moment in the upward position.

9 Inhale as you move the pelvis consciously downward.

10 Repeat upward thrust, letting out a "Ha" sound and exhaling as many times as you feel able.

11 Variation: Instead of an upward thrust, make it a downward thrust movement. Thus, as the buttocks hit the mat/pillow, let out a "Ha" sound. Remember, you can modify the intensity of the thrust in any direction.

12 Slowly lower lower-body, back and buttocks down to the floor. Let arms and hands relax on the floor beside you, legs are stretched out. Breathe deeply several times. Enjoy.

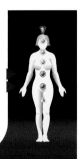

Energy & Consciousness *The above pelvic thrusts are variations on the same theme. The pelvic area is energetically nourished by the second chakra. This has to do with our creativity and our sexuality. Because of the various taboos in our culture, the genital area is usually the place where one feels shame and embarrassment as a child. In consciously moving the pelvis, we could feel emotions such as anger or shame, as well as experiencing a sense of power and pleasure. When we can let go of the shame and simply just feel, most people feel good and also feel a sense of strength when doing the pelvic thrust. It loosens up the lower part of the body and allows the energy to flow more. Energy that moves and flows helps keep the body healthy. Stagnant energy, like stagnant water, can promote illnesses.*

1 Stand with feet spread apart at a comfortable distance. Feet are parallel to each other. Knees are slightly bent. Hips are being comfortably supported by legs. The abdomen is relaxed, as is the rest of the upper body. The head is naturally facing forward. Arms are relaxed on either side of the body.

4 In the bent FORWARD position, slowly begin to move upper body toward the LEFT side. Try to only move at the waist.

5 Continue to move your upper body to LEFT, then toward the BACK and toward the RIGHT.

6 Change directions.

2 Place hands on either side of your waist.

7 Start slowly, feeling and noticing any tension in every move.

8 Keep breathing throughout.

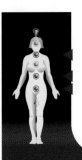

3 Slowly bend upper body forward. Head and neck are relaxed and move in the direction of the torso movement.

Energy & Consciousness *We are mobilizing the lower half of our body with this movement. This is from where we support ourselves. At the same time, our head moves like a periscope leading the way, and our upper body slowly takes on the movement as well. The activated chakras are the second, third, and fifth in front and sixth in the back. As you do these movements, do you feel steady, do you feel sturdy? Is your base strong, or a little fragile? Pay attention to subtleties. How does it feel to be slowly moving your waist and hips? Is there a tightness or do the movements flow?*

1 Lying down on back. Knees are bent; feet are parallel to each other on the ground, spread apart at a comfortable distance, wider than shoulder-width apart. Lower back is touching the ground. The abdomen is relaxed, as is the rest of the upper body. The head is naturally looking toward the ceiling. Neck is relaxed. Arms are relaxed and placed on either side of the body. Breathe naturally.

4 Gradually begin to press the tips of your fingers into your belly. Tenderly move your fingers, while still pressing the tips into your belly, in a clockwise direction beginning at your diaphragm area. You may choose to close your eyes as you massage your belly.

7 Breathe continuously throughout the massage.

8 Repeat the massage movements, but now in a counterclockwise direction.

9 Note: When you find a place of tension, breathe deeply a couple of times and relax. Notice if the tension dissipates or not after that.

2 Place the palms of both hands on your lower belly.

3 Breathe deeply 2 or 3 times.

5 Your fingers together are making a circular motion in each of the four quadrants of your belly.

6 Gently press your fingers deeper to feel and release any tension as you circle around the belly.

Energy & Consciousness *The belly is a unique area, because our unconscious feelings of sorrow, anger and depression tend to accumulate there. With this massage, we begin to get in touch with those feelings that we did not connect with earlier. In this way, as you massage your belly, you may begin to feel sad, cry or be outright angry. As you feel your feelings, allow your breath to move naturally. Just notice what is taking place and where your feelings want to lead you. Later, you may decide to reflect on what feelings came up for you during the massage and their meaning for you.*

4. Chest

The chest is where we take in the air or energy that is often called Prana, or the life force. Is your breathing shallow or is it full? Are you getting from the air the nourishment that you need to sustain and enrich the beautiful person that you are? And your heart, do you feel tension in your chest? Often we shield our heart with muscular armor, holding back or protecting our feelings. The following movements will help to begin to soften the armor and to expand your breathing to take in more of the life energy that is continuously available to you. It will also give you an opportunity to express your anger in a way that is healthy, as well as to open your heart a little more. As you expand and fill your chest, feel more present, more alive and more abundant, you will long to share more of who you are and the love that you carry in your heart with yourself, with the world.

THE ACTIVATING BREATH
SELF-EMBRACE
GET OFF MY BACK
HEART TO HEART
HEART ABOVE HEAD
THE PULSATION OF YOUR BEING
OPEN CHEST
RIB CAGE EXPANSION
NOURISHING BREATH
BACK STRETCH
BACK-TO-BACK MASSAGE
OPEN TORSO TWIST

1 Standing position. Stand with feet shoulder-width apart. Feet are parallel to each other. Knees are slightly bent. Hips are being comfortably supported by legs. The abdomen is relaxed, as is the rest of the upper body. The head is naturally facing forward. Arms are relaxed on either side of the body. Breathe naturally.

2 While standing, inhale in 5 rhythmic intakes: inhale 1, inhale 2, inhale 3, inhale 4, and inhale 5. Make sure you hold your breath and do not exhale between intakes.

3 While inhaling in the 5 rhythmic intakes, arch back and move flexed arms towards the back, so that elbows move toward each other to meet at your back, increasing the arch of the spine. Doing this will open the upper chest for an increase in the air flowing into the upper cavity of the lungs.

4 Once you have inhaled in 5 rhythmic intakes, hold the breath until the *The Saturation Point* (until you can no longer stand holding the breath in and thus feel that you *must* exhale).

5 When you reach the *The Saturation Point*, consciously and forcefully expel the exhaling breath out, in one strong count, with a resounding "Ha" sound.

6 As you exhale, thrust the pelvis forward while contracting the belly and squeezing the perineum (area between the genitals and the anus).

7 Repeat initially 5 times. See if through time you can work up to 100 plus repetitions.

8 By breathing in this manner you are bringing the LIFE FORCE into YOU!

9 Note: This breathing exercise can be done laying down as well. However, you must keep your knees bent, feet to the ground. While inhaling, the lower back will be off the ground due to the arching of the back, for the expansion of the chest. The pressure of the upper body will be on the upper part of the shoulders. On the exhalation, the lower back and buttocks will touch the floor and the pelvis will tip forward. Use a cushion under the buttocks if you choose to do this exercise while laying down.

Energy & Consciousness *Breathing in this manner, you are bringing additional oxygen to your brain and the rest of your body. It is an expansive movement. This aids in our level of consciousness and presence in the here and now. With this exercise, we energize our fifth and sixth chakras, which nourish our lower brain, ears and nose, as well as our nervous system.*

1 Stand or sit comfortably.

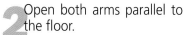

2 Open both arms parallel to the floor.

3 Place LEFT arm over RIGHT.

4 LEFT hand reaches behind RIGHT shoulder.

5 RIGHT hand reaches behind LEFT shoulder.

6 Breathe and enjoy the warmth of the embrace.

7 If you would like, you can tuck your head into your chest, for a stronger feeling of coziness with yourself.

8 Breathe a few times for your own pleasure and nourishment.

9 Slowly open arms wide, palms open facing forward. Take a few deep breaths.

10 Feel the pleasure of the openness of your chest, its strength and its vulnerability.

11 Switch arms that will embrace now.

12 Place RIGHT arm over LEFT.

13 Repeat the embrace as many times as you would like.

Energy & Consciousness *The Self-Embrace stimulates the opening and stretching of the shoulder blades. The heart chakra, at the back, has to do with one's will, and in this case, the will of the heart. Our heart chakra in front has to do with feelings like love. Can you receive the love you have within and direct it toward yourself and others? Do you want to? What keeps you from sharing more your love and of yourself?*

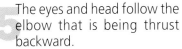

1 Stand with feet spread apart at a comfortable distance, wider than shoulder-width apart. Feet are parallel to each other. Knees are comfortably bent. Hips are being comfortably supported by legs. The abdomen is relaxed, as is the rest of the upper body. The head is naturally facing forward. Arms are relaxed on either side of the body. Breathe naturally.

5 The eyes and head follow the elbow that is being thrust backward.

2 Bend arms at a 90-degree angle and make fists with your hands.

3 Initiate the movement by slowly alternating thrusting the RIGHT and then the LEFT elbow as far back as possible. For this, the waist will rotate.

4 With every thrust of an elbow back, let out a resounding "Ha" sound, or you can choose to say "Get off my back," "Leave me alone," or any other phrase that has meaning to you.

6 Start out slowly and gradually increase the intensity of the thrust, the waist rotation and the opening of the sound.

7 Return to a standing position and breathe deeply, relishing the freeing up of the tension in the musculature, the heart and mind.

 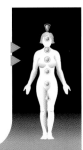

Energy & Consciousness *This movement stimulates the opening of the chest, voice and diaphragm. Since the feeling center is in front, we are opening up this center as well. It frees up our emotions. Try to get in touch with your feelings as you are doing this exercise. Who or what did you want to leave you alone, or to get off your back? Is there anything that needs freeing up in your present life?*

1 Facing your partner, stand with feet spread apart at a comfortable distance.

2 Feet are parallel to each other. Knees are slightly bent. Hips are being comfortably supported by legs. The abdomen is relaxed, as is the rest of the upper body. The head is naturally facing forward. Arms are relaxed on either side of the body.

3 Breathe naturally a few times with your eyes closed.

4 Open your eyes and face your partner.

5 You and your partner hold each other's hands at chest height.

6 Look into each other's eyes.

7 Both begin to show and verbally express anger, through facial expressions, sounds, words and movements, but continue to keep hands clasped together.

8 Pause and breathe for a brief moment yet still in energetic and hand-to-hand contact with your partner.

9 Now both partners begin to show and verbally express love. Show your partner who you really are, through facial expressions, sounds, words and movements, but continue to keep hands clasped together.

10 Keep hands and feet moving, gently.

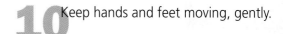

11 Notice. Receive.

12 Perceive what is happening within you.

13 Still holding hands with partner, stretch arms outward to the sides parallel to the ground, opening up so that your chest is touching your partner's chest: heart to heart.

14 Breathe. Feel each other's heart.

15 Remain in this open, flowing position. Now slowly bend knees and stay on knees while touching heart to heart. Feel each other's heart, feel each other's breath.

16 Embrace.

17 Breathe deeply.

18 Share with each other what this experience was like for each one of you.

Energy & Consciousness *We are softening the energetic protective cover over your heart with this exercise. Feel the energy of this meeting of hearts with your partner and enjoy the sweetness of it. What does the expression "openhearted" mean to you? What does it look like to be openedhearted? How does it feel? How can you carry openheartedness into your daily life?*

1 Place yourself comfortably on your knees.

5 Slowly move arms to the sides of the body and breathe.

6 Notice the beating of your heart and the rhythm of your breath.

2 Slowly bend the upper body forward so that forehead meets the ground. (If unable to place forehead on the ground, place a pillow or towel propped up so that head can be supported).

7 Allow the beating of the heart to take over the chatting of the mind and permeate your breath and body.

8 Savour this moment.

3 Arms are stretched forward as far as possible.

4 Breathe deeply.

9 While still kneeling, slowly raise your upper body. Start with your lower back, one vertebra at a time, leaving the head to be the last to rise.

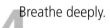

Energy & Consciousness *The heart and the forehead are moving in the direction of touching the ground and grounding. As we bring our attention to our heart and our breath, our heart can open wider, and our breathing can relax even more. The heart is the center of where we feel love. The forehead or the sixth chakra has to do with how a person sees reality or how he sees the world and how he believes the world will see him. As you get up, be aware of your feelings and how they color what you perceive within and without.*

1 Choose a comfortable position. Standing, sitting or laying down.

2 Be in that position for a few minutes simply breathing in silence with your eyes closed.

3 Place your RIGHT palm facing the chest, upon your heart.

4 Continue to breathe naturally, without tensing your belly.

5 Tune your attention to your heart placed under your RIGHT palm.

6 Breathe and gradually begin to pick up the rhythm of your heart beat.

7 Can you feel your heartbeat? What is its beat like?

8 Continue sensing and perceiving your heartbeat while breathing naturally.

9 Begin to sound out your heartbeat. Don't be embarrassed. It is your heart's voice.

10 Sound it out in your own voice (whether it be a tum, tum tum; or pa, pa, pa, pa, pa; or whichever way it sounds to you—there is no right or wrong heartbeat sound).

11 Once you feel that you are in continued contact with your heartbeat, voice your heartbeat's rhythm out loud confidently.

12 You may open your eyes and perceive if there is a difference in your being able to stay in contact with your heartbeat.

13 Gradually move into a standing position, if you are not already standing.

14 Begin to walk with the same beat of your heart, while voicing your heartbeat's rhythm out loud.

15 Play a little bit with the intensity of your vocalization of the heartbeat. Make it gradually stronger and higher and then gradually lighter and lower.

16 Slowly stand and notice if you are able to continue in contact with your heartbeat, without voicing the heartbeat or even keeping your RIGHT palm over your heart.

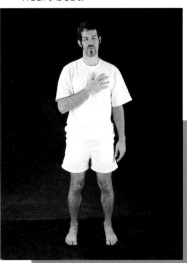

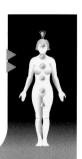

Energy & Consciousness *How aware are we of the rhythm of our beings, the rhythm of our hearts? Our hearts are the materialization of the impulse of our being into this world. This is the impulse that sustains, nourishes and encourages life to move onward physically, emotionally, energetically and spiritually. This is the pulsation that carries forth your love and joy. How much love and joy do you experience in your life? How much more would you like to experience? Are you open to receiving it?*

1 Stand with feet shoulder-width apart. Feet are parallel to each other. Knees are slightly bent. Hips are being comfortably supported by legs. The abdomen is relaxed, as is the rest of the upper body. The head is naturally facing forward. Arms are relaxed on either side of the body.

2 Breathe deeply a few times.

3 Relax the shoulders. Extend both arms forward. Hands in fists.

4 Move the elbows toward the back in an attempt to make them touch each other.

5 Hold elbows pressed back for a count of 10.

6 Hold your breath while doing the countdown.

7 Release the breath while slowly bringing the elbows forward to rest by your side.

8 Stand in the initial position.

9 Repeat this movement a few times and notice how your capacity to hold your chest open for longer periods of time increases each time you do it.

Energy & Consciousness *Experience being open. How does that feel? Do you feel vulnerable with your chest open? Are you open to feeling open? Or does it bring up the feeling of fear? Notice what this movement brings up for you and what you want to do with it.*

1 Stand or sit comfortably.

2 Place hands on either side of your rib cage.

3 Breathe from the belly, filling *The Breath Path* with your breath.

4 Notice through your touch your own breathing rhythm and the expansion and compression of your rib cage.

5 Gradually deepen the breath, exhaling from the mouth with a deep "Ha" sigh.

6 As the rib cage expands with the inhalation, your hands follow the expansion.

7 As the rib cage contracts with the exhalation, your hands compress the rib cage, assisting in the exhalation.

8 Repeat this movement as many times as you would like.

9 Relax and enjoy the sense of fulfillment and plenitude.

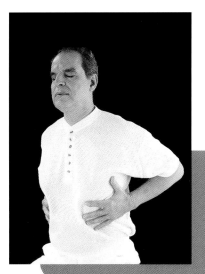

Energy & Consciousness *This very simple and subtle movement enables you to make contact with yourself in the most basic way by connecting you with your breathing rhythm. In moments of despair, feeling fear, overwhelmed or feeling like you have no control of the circumstances, this exercise will give you grounding and bring you to a place of feeling more secure and more sure of yourself.*

1 In a laying down position knees are bent; feet are parallel to each other on the ground, comfortably placed. Lower back is touching the ground. The abdomen is relaxed, as is the rest of the upper body. The head is naturally looking toward the ceiling. Neck is relaxed. Arms are relaxed on either side of the body. Breathe naturally.

4 As you continue to inhale, allow the air to *fill* and *visibly* expand your belly, diaphragm area, chest and lower neck —what we call *The Breath Path*.

2 Gently place both palms on lower abdomen close to the genital area.

5 Both palms follow *The Breath Path* as you inhale and expand the areas with your breath.

3 While breathing deeply from the belly, allow the belly to rise as you inhale.

6 When your expanding inhaling breath and your palms have reached your lower neck, hold both palms in place for a brief second and breathe.

7 Now slowly exhale from your mouth, while letting out a prolonged "Ha" sound as you gradually flatten the chest, diaphragm and belly (in that order).

8 On the exhalation, your palms slowly retrace *The Breath Path,* starting at the neck and downward, to once again reach and rest on the lower belly. You have done one complete breath.

9 This is a continuous movement, as the palms follow the inhaling and exhaling of the breath from our bodies.

10 Maintain the pleasurable breathing rhythm by starting out with four complete breaths.

11 Note: We suggest that this movement be enjoyed with your eyes closed. This will encourage the increase of the depth of perception of your breathing following *The Breath Path.*

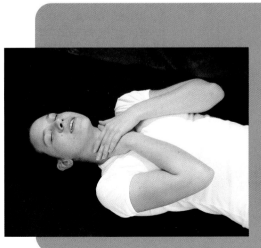

Energy & Consciousness *This is more of a movement than an exercise. It involves paying attention to our body and to our breathing. How does your body respond when it takes in air and when it releases it? It is a lot like life when we give and when we take, and we give again and we take again. It also could remind you of the ebb and the flow of the waves on the beach. What kinds of things ebb and flow in and out of your life? What kind of thoughts and feelings? The giving and taking movements might instill a gentle sense of confidence, like "I can trust that I will receive and I can also give." Does it seem strange to realize that breathing nourishes us? Conscious breathing can increase the quality of our energy as well as the quantity.*

1 Stand back to back with partner, feet spread apart at a comfortable distance

2 Feet are parallel to each other. Knees are slightly bent. Hips are being comfortably supported by legs. The abdomen is relaxed, as is the rest of the upper body. The head is naturally facing forward. Arms are relaxed on either side of the body.

3 Breathe naturally a few times.

4 Choose who will do the back stretch first. The person chosen will be PARTNER A. The remaining person will be PARTNER B.

5 PARTNER B will be the one assisting PARTNER A's back stretch.

6 When both partners are ready, interlock elbows.

7 PARTNER B must keep legs bent and feet parallel to each other while breathing naturally throughout the *Back Stretch*.

8 PARTNER B bends forward while slowly moving PARTNER A up PARTNER B's back, thus stretching PARTNER A's back.

9 PARTNER A must surrender to the stretch, relaxing the abdomen, neck, lower back, and legs, while letting the breathing move effortlessly.

10 PARTNER B, who is supporting PARTNER A's body, ensures that PARTNER A's buttocks are above PARTNER B's for a deeper and safer stretch.

11 PARTNER B and PARTNER A stay in this stretching position for as long as PARTNER A will stand.

12 Once PARTNER A signals to PARTNER B that the stretch is over, PARTNER B will gradually raise the torso, while maintaining the knees bent, so that PARTNER A's feet can reach the ground and gradually stand up

13 Back to back, both partners take a few deep breaths.

14 PARTNER A may want to bend upper body forward to elongate the back after this deep stretch.

15 Breathe.

16 Repeat the same movement but now with PARTNER B experiencing the back stretch and PARTNER A supporting it.

17 Note: It is important to be more or less the same size for this exercise. I remember the first time I did this, (and it is easier than it sounds), I felt a sense of power knowing that I could support another person in this manner.

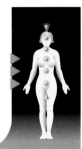

Energy & Consciousness *Energetically, the back chakras open. The back chakras are related to our will. The diaphragm and heart chakras in the front open as well. It takes the will of the heart to trust and surrender to another in order to do this exercise as well as a sense of adventure. Where in your life are you trusting and where to you want to keep control at all times? In what areas of your life would you stretch a little bit further out of your comfort zone, both personally and professionally?*

1 Take a few deep breaths.

2 Standing back to back with partner, keep knees slightly bent.

3 Gently begin to rub, wiggle, caress and press against your partner's back so that: buttocks to buttocks, lower back to lower back, then middle-back to middle-back, then further up, shoulder to shoulder, neck to neck, head to head are massaging each other.

4 Giggle, breathe and enjoy the contact and the feelings that come up.

5 Relax, let yourself give and receive from your partner. How does it feel?

6 Notice your own body and the presence of your partner's body and energy. Notice where you begin and end and where you and your partner share a common space and where your partner is.

7 Go back to witnessing your own energy and body. Breathe.

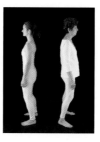

8 Now each one takes a step forward. Feel if you can maintain contact with your partner as you slowly physically distance yourself.

9 Could you maintain contact with your own energy and self as well as your partner's or did you lose it?

10 Take another step forward. Mentally and energetically check your connection with partner.

54

11 Turn to face partner. Look at your partner in the eyes.

12 Take a step toward partner while looking at her. How do you feel?

13 Share with each other feelings and impressions.

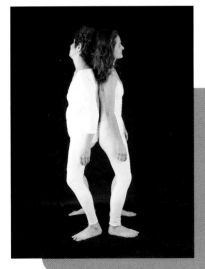

Energy & Consciousness *This exercise brings up several elements. One is the experience of both giving and receiving at almost the same time. That is totally engaging. Do you like it? Is it easy to give but not to receive, or is it the other way around, easier to receive but harder to give? Were you playful or serious during the exercise? We are working with our feeling centers. How did this affect you? Does contact mean you have to be physically touching, or can you still feel the contact when you move away? Are you feeling vulnerable at this time? Is this an exercise you would like to try again?*

1 Stand comfortably with legs slightly bent.

2 Arms are open wide to the sides, parallel to the floor.

3 While breathing deeply, slowly rotate your torso as far as possible to the RIGHT.

4 Arms remain parallel to the ground, eyes and head follow the rotation.

5 Pause at your maximum rotation.

6 Breathe a couple of deep breaths.

7 Gradually return to face forward. Arms remain outstretched.

8 Repeat rotation to the LEFT side.

9 Start slow and increase the speed and intensity as you feel you are able to.

10 Notice if your initial maximum rotation increases as you repeat the movement.

11 Note: This movement can be done in pairs as well. In that case, the partners pair up back to back, arms outstretched, parallel to the ground, hands clasping. They choose which side they will rotate to first. Pause, breathe. Then switch sides. It is important to be aware of one's own as well as one's partner's physical and mental limits and take them into consideration when doing movements in partnership.

This twisting movement opens the sacral area and again the second chakra. It can do wonders for those who have lower back pain, which often exists because of stress and the inability to relax that area. Being stubborn also can increase lower back pain for some people.

5. Arms & Shoulders

It is with the upper part of our body that we make contact with others. Without our arms, hands and fingers, contact is more difficult. With our arms, we can reach out to others, and up toward the Divine. Are your shoulders healthy and strong? Does your body sway forward, or is it erect? We use our hands to make gestures, to explain ourselves. Are you conscious of your upper body and how it feels? These exercises can increase your awareness of the difficulty or ease you might have to reach out to others, as well as accepting help from others. As you move with these exercises, your ability and awareness of the principle of giving and receiving and what is necessary to make them happen will broaden.

1 Stand or sit comfortably. The abdomen is relaxed, as is the rest of the upper body. The head is naturally facing forward. Arms are relaxed on either side of the body.

2 Relax the shoulders. Breathe deeply a few times.

3 Place arms outstretched, parallel to the ground.

4 Palms are facing upward.

5 Bend one finger at a time toward the center of the palm. Start with the pinky and end with the thumb.

6 Work the same finger on both hands simultaneously.

7 With each finger bent, inhale.

8 Exhale only at the end, when all 10 fingers are in tight fists.

9 Repeat the sequence *twice*.

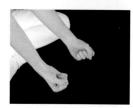

10 Relax arms.

11 Take a few deep breaths.

Energy & Consciousness *This is the part of our body, the upper part, that includes our third, fourth and fifth chakras. We use our arms to reach out and communicate with others. We use our upper torso to touch and connect with others. The movement of arms outstretched in a horizontal position opens us to the world. If we do this and look upward, we are opening to the heavens, to the stars, even to the Divine.*

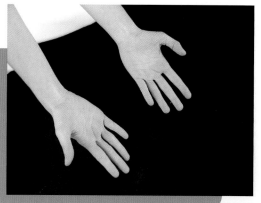

1 Stand or sit comfortably.

2 Take 3 or 4 deep breaths.

3 Stretch both arms in front of body, parallel to floor.

4 Hands are spread open; palms are facing outward, away from the body. Fingers pointing toward the ceiling.

5 LEFT hand presses the RIGHT hand fingers, backward, toward RIGHT hand's wrist.

6 Breathe deeply, exhaling with a "Ha" sigh.

7 Release the pressure.

8 Now rotate RIGHT hand, so that palm continues to face outward, fingers pointing toward the floor.

9 LEFT hand pulls RIGHT hand fingers toward the RIGHT wrist.

10 Breathe deeply, exhaling with a "Ha" sigh.

11 Release the pressure.

12 Repeat *Finger, Wrist and Tendon Stretch* to LEFT hand.

Energy & Consciousness *This stretch opens up the energy and acupuncture lines. Our fingers and wrists rotate and also go back and forth. In Spanish the word for wrist is muneca, which is also the same word used for doll or puppet. I imagine because a wrist can move in many directions for the puppet to move. It can flip and flop. The fingers, when brought together in certain configurations, allow us to express ourselves in art, music and the written word. Our hands are an important instrument for communication with the world.*

1 Stand comfortably before your partner and take 3 deep breaths.

2 Choose who will do the exercise first. The person chosen will be PARTNER A. The remaining person will be PARTNER B.

3 PARTNER A stands before PARTNER B at a far enough distance that PARTNER A's outstretched arm does not quite touch PARTNER B's.

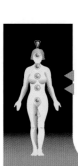

4 PARTNER A reaches with LEFT hand to attempt to touch PARTNER B's hand, while the other hand is behind the back. The purpose for this is so that PARTNER A really feels the stretch. As she stretches, she may lunge with her legs, lay on the floor or whatever is necessary while attempting to reach PARTNER B's hand, by stretching her shoulder, arms and hands.

5 PARTNER A stays with LEFT hand and arm stretching, allowing now that her shoulder reaches out even further.

6 In the meantime, PARTNER B is standing offering her hands to PARTNER A while asking PARTNER A: What do you *really* want? What do you *really* need?

7 PARTNER A continues to stretch until PARTNER A reaches PARTNER B's hand.

8 PARTNER A shares with PARTNER B, while still in position and out loud, what she is reaching for in her life (Love, Support, Help, Attention, Service etc.)

9 Repeat the exercise now with PARTNER B reaching for PARTNER A's hand.

10 Once both PARTNER A and B have completed this exercise, take a moment to share with each other what may have come up.

Energy & Consciousness *Reaching out to get our needs met is often difficult or even impossible for some of us. To do this in life means that we have some degree of trust that our needs will be met. If we have learned when we were very small children that our needs would not be met, it is difficult as an adult to reach out. Are you a person that has difficulty to reach out, or is this easy for you? If so, how can you reach for even more both for you and for others?*

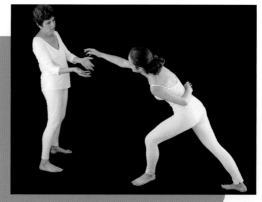

1 Stand comfortably, head facing forward.

2 Take 3 deep breaths.

3 Place hands in boxing position.

4 Start with a RIGHT arm punch.

5 Alternate forward movement of RIGHT and LEFT arm punches.

6 With each punch, exhale with a corresponding and resounding "Ha" sound.

7 Give as many punches as you feel you are able or need to give.

8 If you would like, try to bring to mind a situation that you would like to direct this punching energy toward.

9 Note: The intention for the one doing this exercise is to *direct* one's energy outward and perceive the amount of power one has when focusing energy and action.

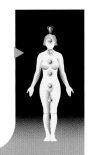

Energy & Consciousness *It feels good to direct energy outward. Does this feel right to you? The chakra that is involved in this movement is the back of the fourth chakra, as well as the fifth chakra when you include the voice. This has to do with the will and going after what we want. How easy is that for you? How clearly do you state and go after what you want without any excuses or diminishing what your goal means to you?*

1 Stand or sit comfortably.

2 Take 3 or 4 deep breaths.

3 Close fingers into very tight fists and press as hard as you can.

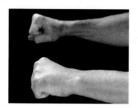

4 Hold to a count down of 10.

5 Quickly release.

6 As you release the tight fist, open hands wide, fingers spread apart.

7 Tighten each hand individually into a fist or both hands simultaneously.

8 Repeat as many times as you would like.

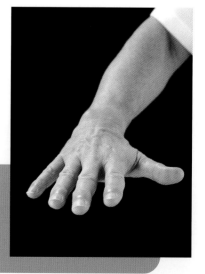

Energy & Consciousness *Energetically we have many smaller chakras on the palms of our hands. For a healer, the energy for healing comes mostly through the hands. Have you ever noticed that when you hurt yourself, get scratched or scraped, you immediately put your hands on the wound? We instinctively know that we are all healers.*

1 Stand with feet shoulder-width apart. Feet are parallel to each other. Knees are slightly bent. Hips are being comfortably supported by legs. The abdomen is relaxed, as is the rest of the upper body. The head is naturally facing forward. Arms are relaxed on either side of the body.

2 Relax the shoulders.

3 Take a deep breath and hold it.

4 Bring both shoulders toward your ears.

5 Hold your shoulders at ear height.

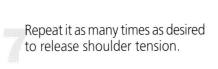

6 Forcefully release the shoulders downward with an open "Ha" sound of relief.

7 Repeat it as many times as desired to release shoulder tension.

This well-known exercise brings energy into the whole upper part of your body. At the same time, notice that your feet are planted on the ground, stabilizing the movement. As your voice makes the "Ha" sound, you can let go and experience relief. It is that simple.

1 Stand with feet shoulder-width apart. Feet are parallel to each other. Knees are slightly bent. Hips are being comfortably supported by legs. The abdomen is relaxed, as is the rest of the upper body. The head is naturally facing forward. Arms are relaxed on either side of the body.

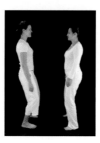  

2 Relax the shoulders.

3 Breathe deeply a few times.

4 Choose a partner.

5 Stand facing your partner.

6 Both you and your partner place hands facing and touching each other at chest level.

7 Look into each other's eyes.

8 Each one starts to push their palms against the palms of the other. *(Depending on how fiercely you engage in this exercise, perhaps you would want to interlace fingers for a greater grip on your partner.)*

9 As you push against the palms of your partner, you may experiment saying: "No," "I want it my way," "It is going to be my way," "You won't get me," "I win," "Get away." Feel free to choose which words to incorporate to this movement.

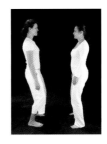

10 Once there is a sense of completion on both parts, slowly come together with hands still interlocked, eyes closed.

11 Take 4 deep breaths together.

12 Take a moment to share what came up during the exercise.

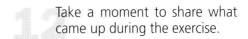

Energy & Consciousness *This simple exercise makes explicit what we sometimes feel but are afraid to say to another person. We do have this lower self part of us that wants to win no matter what, or wants something special for ourselves, yet we are not willing to give it to others. We say that it is OK to express these feelings in this exercise environment, in this way. It is not good for our health when we have feelings that we continuously have to suppress. We also do not feel honest when we know that we have these unexpressed feelings. They can make us feel guilty if never owned and might eventually manifest as a disease.*

1 Stand or sit in a comfortable position.

2 Take 3 or 4 deep breaths.

3 Rub palms together until they are very warm or even hot.

4 Place your palms on your face, or any other part of your body.

5 Breathe as the soothing and healing heat of your hands makes contact with that part of the body.

6 Once the heat has transferred to the chosen area, rub palms again.

7 Reapply to the same area or choose another area.

Energy & Consciousness *The palms of our hands have smaller chakras, so the energy can be transmitted through the touch. This is a way we can consciously care for ourselves. We intuitively use our hands to soothe, calm and caress our loved ones. Our healing hands have great power, for they are one of the channels through which we touch and share our energy with others. By practicing this exercise, we can choose to share our energy with others, as well as with ourselves.*

1 Stand with feet shoulder-width apart. Feet are parallel to each other. Knees are slightly bent. Hips are being comfortably supported by legs. The abdomen is relaxed, as is the rest of the upper body. The head is naturally facing forward. Arms are relaxed on either side of the body.

2 Relax the shoulders.

3 Breathe deeply 5 times.

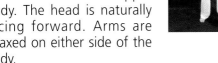

4 Outstretch both arms so that they are parallel to the ground.

5 Cross the arms in front of your chest, RIGHT arm over LEFT. Then switch to crossing LEFT arm over RIGHT.

6 As you are crossing your arms, inhale in 2 counts.

7 Open arms wide as far to the back as possible, parallel to the ground. Chest sways naturally forward. Palms face forward.

8 As you open your arms wide, allow for a sonorous "Ha" sound as you exhale.

9 Repeat this opening movement as many times as you would like.

10 Variation: This exercise can be done with a partner in a seated position, with legs stretched out before you. Your partner will place his bent knee between your shoulder blades and pull your arms, by holding onto your hands, as far back as possible. As your partner is assisting in this stretch, your head is being supported by your partner's upper leg, as you keep your head facing forward. Both keep breathing naturally. Switch partners.

Energy & Consciousness *This exercise opens the chest and the heart chakras. How does it feel when you open your arms wide? Do you feel vulnerable, or are you ready to open your heart to another, to life?*

67

1 Stand with feet shoulder-width apart. Feet are parallel to each other. Knees are slightly bent. Hips are being comfortably supported by legs. The abdomen is relaxed, as is the rest of the upper body. The head is naturally facing forward. Arms are relaxed on either side of the body.

2 Relax the shoulders.

3 Breathe deeply 5 times.

4 Begin raising your arms to the ceiling. Arms are parallel, by the side of each ear.

5 Continue to breathe naturally and evenly.

6 Slowly include your fingers in your reaching toward the ceiling, stretching them further so that, just maybe, they will reach the ceiling.

7 When you cannot reach any further with your arms and fingers, slowly fold your arms at the elbows.

8 In a completely relaxing manner, let the arms and hands flop down at the shoulder to then fall to the sides of the body. This is one flowing movement. It is as if once you were not able to reach the ceiling, after having built up the tension in the upper body, you have just "given up" and the arms just flop down to the sides of your body, thus releasing the tension.

9 Repeat this movement 3 or 4 times.

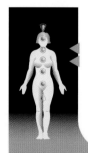

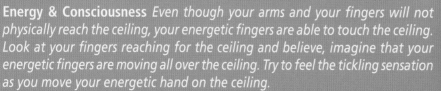

Energy & Consciousness *Even though your arms and your fingers will not physically reach the ceiling, your energetic fingers are able to touch the ceiling. Look at your fingers reaching for the ceiling and believe, imagine that your energetic fingers are moving all over the ceiling. Try to feel the tickling sensation as you move your energetic hand on the ceiling.*

1 Stand in a comfortable position. Neck and shoulders relaxed.

2 Inhale as you gradually raise your RIGHT arm, hand open, fingers outstretched as if you were going to "pick" an imaginary prize, something that you deeply long for, from the sky.

3 Reach up as far as possible, so as to stand on the tip of your toes and continue stretching to the maximum. *Do not release your breath yet.*

4 Grasp your longing with your RIGHT hand and bring it toward the floor.

5 As your hand touches the floor, release your breath with a forceful "Ha" sound.

6 Go back to the initial standing position and take a few deep, relaxing breaths.

7 Repeat movement with the LEFT arm.

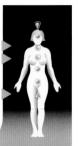

8 Repeat movement 3 times with each arm, while keeping in mind at all times that which you long to have, do, create and or be, as you reach toward your longing and ground it into your life.

Energy & Consciousness *Reaching up stretches the front of the body, which is the feeling center. At the same time, it also stretches the will center in the back. This combination is very useful as we can see, because we can feel in our body that we have what we need to go after what we desire. This exercise is an experiential analogy of consciously moving in the direction of your longing, reaching it and making it real. That is, grounding your longing into the present moment. Once this is done, it is no longer a dream but a reality which you can savor, grow with and, if you choose, share with those around you. So ask yourself, what is it that I really desire at this time in my life? How would my life be any different if I were to have it? So what keeps me from connecting with my longing and making it real in my life today?*

1 Sit with legs straight and arms outstretched forward, parallel to ground.

2 Place a pillow or cushion on your lap.

3 With hands in fists, begin punching the cushion.

4 As you punch, say: "No," "I am not willing to give you anything," "I will not let you near," "Go away" and etc. Try to focus your attention on life situations or circumstances that are relevant to you and which you would like to push away, out of your life, far from you.

5 Note: This exercise can be done in pairs. In this case, one of the partners would be holding a pillow or mattress against which the other partner can punch and kick.

Energy & Consciousness *Many times we keep ourselves away from others or experiences, holding ourselves away from life in a passive manner. This exercise physically illustrates this holding life at an arm's length by making us conscious of this life choice through actively pushing life away. This can reveal to us some of the ways we say NO to life. Life is not shutting us out; rather we are shutting out life. Once we are aware of this, then we can decide to actively seek to share and to open ourselves more to life, or to continue shut down. When we are aware, we have a choice.*

6. Neck & Throat

Before you start doing these movements move your attention to your neck and throat, and take a moment to ask yourself how your neck and throat feel? Is your neck relaxed, or is it tight and stiff? How about your throat? Is it clear and open? Make a sound. How does it come out? For many people, this area is challenging. Since our neck is the pathway between our belly and heart to our head, it can be stiff and tight as a way to slow down or hold on to feelings before they can be translated into thoughts in our brain. Our throat can also be tight, trying not to say or express our true feelings.

We know many people who habitually clear their throat before speaking, almost as if they were asking permission to speak. Inwardly, there is fear; fear of being seen, fear of speaking their truth, or fear of asserting themselves. The exercises in this segment will give you the opportunity to try some movements that might not feel familiar. If this is new for you, we invite you to risk trying something new. At the same time, be patient and allow yourself to be more and more present.

1 Choose a comfortable sitting or kneeling position.

2 Breathe naturally throughout the exercise.

3 Gently close your eyes.

4 Start with the mouth closed.

5 Bring attention to your mouth.

6 Perceive whether your teeth are clenched, tight against each other.

7 Relax your jaw and tongue.

8 Gradually bring tongue forward out of your mouth, as if you would like your tongue to reach the tip of your chin.

9 As tongue moves outward and forward, open and widen eyes.

16 Repeat 2 or 3 times.

17 Breathe naturally.

18 Relax.

10 Hold tongue out of the mouth at your extreme position.

11 Your eyes are as widely open as possible.

12 Hold for a count of 10.

13 Slowly retract the tongue back into your mouth, as the eyes simultaneously and gradually close.

14 Remain a few moments with the eyes and mouth closed.

15 Could you feel the stretch? How did it feel?

Energy & Consciousness *This stretch energizes the fifth and sixth chakra. The processes of assimilation and speaking our truth activate the fifth chakra. This has to do with our feelings and our reasoning. This is a good combination. It is important to keep these two centers in balance. Our Western culture has a tendency to be more in the reasoning center and less in the emotional center. With this exercise, we will create a greater balance between the two centers.*

1 In a standing position, place your RIGHT hand on your head and tilt your head toward your RIGHT shoulder.

2 Breathe naturally.

3 Repeat with LEFT hand directing the head toward the LEFT shoulder, while your face is facing forward.

4 With both hands, guide your head FOREWARD so that your chin reaches your chest.

5 Return to center position, head facing forward.

6 Breathe 3 deep breaths.

7 Note: Try to keep your back as straight as possible as you stretch your neck.

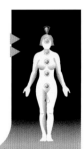

Energy & Consciousness *When we get stressed and anxious, usually our neck and shoulders feel it first. They get stiff and tense up. This blocks the flow of energy to the head. When we do the above exercise, our neck and shoulders begin to relax and our head feels lighter. The energy flows to the head and to our brain. Energetically, we are helping to open or let the energy flow through our fifth and sixth chakra. The fifth chakra has to do with being able to speak our truth, and nourishes our thyroid gland, and the sixth chakra has to do with our ability to visualize things, particularly ideas and concepts.*

1 Stand with feet shoulder-width apart. Feet are parallel to each other. Knees are slightly bent. Hips are being comfortably supported by legs. The abdomen is relaxed, as is the rest of the upper body. The head is naturally facing forward. Arms are relaxed on either side of the body.

2 Relax your shoulders.

3 Take 4 deep breaths.

4 Raise both arms and cradle the back of your neck, with your hands interlaced.

5 Feel your neck being supported by your hands and the warmth they provide to this part of your body.

6 While keeping your shoulders relaxed, take 2 deep breaths.

7 Gradually bend your head forward, chin reaching for the chest. *(For a deeper stretch, bring your hands to the top of your head and press downward.)*

8 Maintain your back straight.

9 Hold the stretch for 5 counts, while breathing naturally.

10 Release your hands from your neck or top of your head.

11 Gently raise your head to its natural, center position.

12 Now tilt your head backward, as far as possible, while breathing naturally.

13 Hold for a count of 5.

14 Return to center position.

15 Slowly turn head to the RIGHT.
Hold for a count of 5.
Breathe naturally.

16 Return to center position.

17 Slowly turn head to the LEFT.
Hold for a count of 5.

18 Breathe naturally.

19 Return to center position.

20 Now begin by slowly tilting your head forward and moving into a smooth rolling of the head to the RIGHT, BACK, LEFT, FORWARD and back to center.

21 Repeat this movement in a counterclockwise direction.

22 Feel the cracks, sounds, stretches that pop up as you gently roll your head in this manner.

23 Repeat 3 times, alternating directions.

24 Return to center.

25 Take 2 deep breaths.

Energy & Consciousness *Do you remember anyone calling you a pain in the neck? What did that mean? These rotations help relax the neck muscles and keep you from feeling the stiffness that can occur. These movements affect the fifth chakra, both front and back. This chakra is very important, because it affects our voice, our lungs and our ability to share and communicate to the world who we are and what we stand for. When this chakra, front and back, is open and functioning, we take responsibility for getting what we need and no longer need to blame others for what we do not have. This chakra also relates to our profession and how we are seen in society.*

1. Face partner in a standing position. Breathe deeply 4 times.

2. Each partner holds the end of a sheet, towel or rope.

3. Each one begins to tug at the sheet, trying to get as much of it from the other partner as possible.

4. Partners begin to struggle for a while, consciously moving and shaking the sheet. As the partners struggle, they look into each other's eyes saying that *"it is mine," "I want it," "give it to me,"* or any other expression that feels pertinent to each partner at the time.

5. Once partners have exhausted the struggle, be it if one "wins" the sheet, or the other "gives up" the sheet, or through mutual agreement to stop the struggle, both choose who will be PARTNER A and who will be PARTNER B.

6. Partners sit down somewhere where PARTNER A's back is supported.

7. PARTNER B lies down between PARTNER A's legs, letting PARTNER B's head rest on PARTNER A's chest.

8. PARTNER A holds PARTNER B.

9. Breathe deeply and spontaneously.

10. PARTNER A places RIGHT hand on PARTNER B's heart.

11. PARTNER B melts into PARTNER A's warm embrace.

12. Continue to breathe spontaneously.

13. When PARTNER B is ready to come out of the embrace, switch.

14. PARTNER B now holds PARTNER A while placing his RIGHT hand on PARTNER A's heart.

15. PARTNER B melts into PARTNER A's warm embrace and continues to breathe.

16. Close this moment when the pairs feel ready.

17. Share with each other what was felt and experienced.

Energy & Consciousness *This exercise engages your whole body physically during the struggle. The feeling "I want it and I'm going to take it" can be strong, or it can be weak. What is your experience? We struggle, we begin to relax, and if we open emotionally, we can receive, or we can give. We do this with our will and our emotions. As we learn more about our emotions and how we work, we become more responsible for our outcomes in life.*

1 Stand in a group circle.

2 Gradually the individuals in the group start moving in various directions.

3 While moving around the room randomly, each person is invited to pound, with fist or palm of hand, on her chest and say: *"I am here!"*

4 Have the group experiment with various intonations, levels of expressiveness, intensity of belief and perceive the differences in their bodies, emotions and minds.

5 Notice if you really meant what you were saying from the first time you said it. Or did it take some time to feel the statement to be true to you? Or do you feel it at all, that is, to be here, in the present? Can you own your own space here and now?

6 Share your experience in pairs or triads.

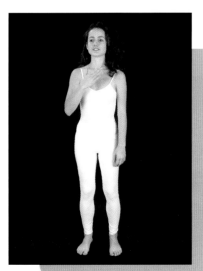

Energy & Consciousness *This exercise, like many of the others, gives us an opportunity to take a position physically, emotionally and mentally that we do not normally take in our present social life, and to consciously stay in the present moment. To walk around in a strutting manner with our friends and family members saying, "I am here," or "I am good" or "I am wonderful" is not a common thing to do. Yet, we might sometimes think that way, or we might feel the opposite. How do we experience this opportunity? Are you embarrassed by it, afraid to say these words out loud? Are you shy, or do you really enjoy saying these words and trying them on like kids trying on grown-ups' clothes to play? What was your experience? How about the others in your group?*

1 Choose a comfortable sitting or laying down position.

2 Breathe deeply a few times. You may choose to do the Nourishing Breath exercise at this time and then follow the instructions below.

3 Ask yourself: What is the meaning of my name? What is the meaning of my childhood nickname? Is there a story to your name? Do you like or dislike your name? Why? When you say your name out loud, how do you feel? How does your body react when you say your name? Or when someone else says it? Is there a difference? Do you like the way it sounds? Does it reflect how you perceive yourself to be? How has your name influenced or affected you in your life?

4 Let the images come to your *mind's eye* (sixth chakra). Allow for your feelings and intuitions to be present.

5 Reflect for a few minutes about who you are. Where do you come from? Who are your parents? Siblings? Where do they come from? What do you stand for in your life? Who do you want to become? Pause and breathe. *You may choose to place your hand on your heart during this reflection.*

6 Continue to breathe and notice what is happening to your body as you reflect on these questions.

7 When you are ready, slowly return your awareness to your surroundings. Smile, breathe deeply, let out a deep sigh and stretch.

8 Immediately write down your reflections when you have completed this exercise. Then choose someone, preferably in the next 24 hours following the completion of this exercise, with whom you would like to share your reflections.

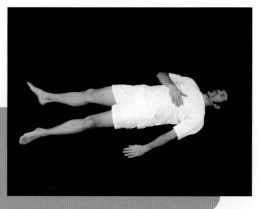

Energy & Consciousness *This can be a waking-up exercise if you are willing to take the time to reflect and to allow your awareness to expand. Life is like a kaleidoscope. When you move the kaleidoscope, even a little bit, the whole picture changes.*

1 Sit comfortably, facing your partner. Your abdomen is relaxed, as is the rest of the upper body. Your head is naturally facing forward. Arms are relaxed on either side of the body.

2 Take 3 deep breaths.

3 Choose, between the two of you, who will do the exercise first.

4 The person chosen will be PARTNER A. The remaining person will be PARTNER B.

5 PARTNER A and PARTNER B gently close eyes to initiate the exercise.

8 Switch.

9 Now PARTNER A listens attentively, with eyes closed, to PARTNER B's voice.

10 Once both PARTNERS have listened to each other, they can now share their impressions with one another.

6 PARTNER A talks, about any topic he chooses to, with eyes closed, while PARTNER B is attentively listening to PARTNER A's voice quality, tone, pitch, seeking to pick up any subtleties.

7 How would PARTNER B describe PARTNER A (physically and personality wise) just by listening to his voice? PARTNER B keeps his impressions to himself. At the end of the exercise, he will then be able to share his impressions with PARTNER A).

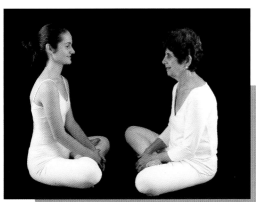

Energy & Consciousness *How much can you tell about another person by just listening to her voice? How does it feel to fully listen to another person? How does it feel to be fully listened to? It has been shown that it is very therapeutic to have someone truly listen to you. What is your experience with your partner doing this exercise?*

1 Choose a comfortable standing or sitting position.

2 Breathe deeply a few times.

3 Place your RIGHT hand (LEFT hand if you are left-handed) on your throat, as if you wanted to hold it with one hand.

4 Swallow 3 or 4 times. Feel the swallowing movement.

5 Place your thumb on one side of the esophagus and the remaining fingers on the other side.

6 Press the esophagus a little bit so that you have a gentle but firm grip on it.

7 Swallow a couple of times.

8 As you swallow, can you feel what is most commonly known as your Adam's apple move up and down?

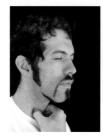 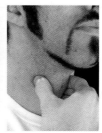

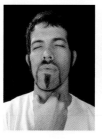 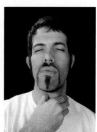

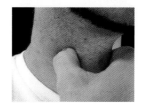

9 Maintaining a gentle but firm hold on your esophagus, gently move your Adam's apple from one side to the other. That is, move it to the RIGHT and then to the LEFT.

10 Slowly move your fingers up and down the throat, from the base of your neck to your jaw, moving the esophagus to the RIGHT and then to the LEFT.

11 Repeat the up and down movements a couple of times.

12 Breathe at a naturally comfortable rhythm throughout the throat massage.

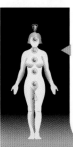 

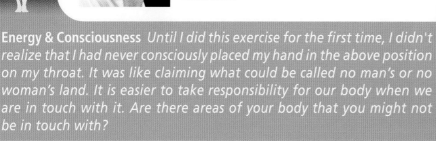

Energy & Consciousness *Until I did this exercise for the first time, I didn't realize that I had never consciously placed my hand in the above position on my throat. It was like claiming what could be called no man's or no woman's land. It is easier to take responsibility for our body when we are in touch with it. Are there areas of your body that you might not be in touch with?*

1 Lie down with your head on your partner's belly.

2 Allow your entire body to relax.

3 Slowly and rhythmically breathe in and out, gradually releasing tension in neck, shoulders, chest, lower back, abdomen, legs and ankles.

4 Once relaxed, tune in to your partner's breathing pattern.

5 Allow your head to rhythmically move up and down according to your partner's own breathing rhythm.

6 Begin by each one of those participating simply letting out a laugh.

7 Feel how it spontaneously becomes a giggle and continues on, being reinforced by the vibration of your partner's laughter on your head, and on and on it goes.

8 Enjoy how contagious the laughter becomes, starting timidly at first and becoming quite loud and outrageous as it progresses.

9 Let the laughter continue to come forth.

10 There will be a moment when it will seem that the pair or group is "all laughed out," and a brief pause will ensue. However, notice that soon enough a new round of laughter may come along.

11 As the pair or group reach a pleasant and spontaneous pause, the pair or group may choose to breathe deeply 3 or 4 times together, letting out a resounding "Ha" sound on the exhale.

12 Relax together for a few minutes.

13 Return gradually to your sitting positions and look into your partner's eyes, or around the group.

14 Notice the radiance on each other's faces and the feeling of closeness and joy that is present in the pair or group.

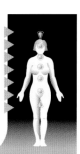

Energy & Counsciousness *Having an experienced facilitator to guide this exercise is important for various reasons, including to have a witness and affirm the group's experience. It is also enjoyable to have one more person to laugh with you.*

7. Jaw & Mouth

The jaw and mouth hold a lot of emotional tension from our early life experiences. The infant uses the jaw and mouth for sucking, and for the infant that means survival. If the mother has not sufficiently nurtured the child, the emotions generated from that loss can still be with us as adults. Is your jaw tight and rigid, or is it flexible and flowing with energy? How about your mouth? Is it relaxed or is it tense? Take a moment and feel your jaw and mouth. How do they feel? The exercises in the following segment will show you how to access some of the answers to these questions. For the most part, they are gentle and explorative. For some, this might be best worked when you are in a more introspective mood.

RAISIN & OLIVE EXPRESSIONS
THE TIGER
LOWER JAW STRETCH
JAW MASSAGE
LIP MOVEMENT
THE SUCKING PAD

1 Stand or sit comfortably.

2 With your eyes closed, bring your attention to your face.

3 Notice any points of tension, numbness or just a "normal" feeling on face, mouth and throat.

4 Breathe deeply 3 or 4 times. Is there any effect on your face?

5 Slowly begin to contract your face, mouth and throat into a *raisin*, wrinkle-like expression. Tighten: jaw, squeeze eyes and throat, frown forehead, press nostrils together, purse lips, tighten tongue against the top of mouth, contract cheeks and clench teeth. Hold your breath.

6 Hold this contracted state for as long as you can.

7 Then quickly release into an *olive* expression.

8 Open eyes and mouth wide, raise up eyebrows, flare nostrils, tongue stretched out, open throat, letting out a strong, open and lingering "Ha" sound.

9 Hold for a count of 5.

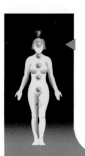

10 Slowly return to natural facial expression.

11 Repeat 2 or 3 times.

12 How do your face, mouth and throat feel like now?

Energy & Consciousness *Energetically, this exercise affects the sixth chakra, also known as the third eye. This chakra can be cleared and strengthened to take in more energy. The movement also stimulates your whole face so that you look more alive. This will also help in your ability to visualize and increase your mental clarity and understanding.*

1 Stand or sit in a comfortable position.

2 Breathe naturally.

3 Warm up the jaw by bringing the lower jaw forward slowly. Try not to move the entire head forward when performing this exercise.

4 Repeat 3 times.

5 On the 4th time, let out a "Ha" sound as the lower jaw is thrust forward.

6 Feel the stretching of the Sternocleidomastoid muscle.

7 Repeat the thrust forward 2 times.

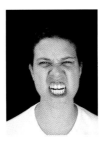

8 Now begin to create facial expressions that reveal your animal, tiger side. Growl and hiss as your face expresses anger.

9 Move your jaw forward, sideways, your eyes and your lips, opening and closing. Experiment with the different sounds that come out as you growl and hiss.

10 Now posture your body for attack. Your hands are shaped into claws, your lower jaw forward, striking out to bite an attacker. This will increase the intensity of the movement as well as bring forth emotional content as you perform the exercise.

11 Grasp with your hands forward. Alternate between grasping with hands and thrusting your jaw forward, attempting to bite.

12 Slowly return to initial position by declawing hands and softening your facial expressions.

13 Notice how your face and upper body are energized and relaxed.

14 Take a moment to breathe and allow for a spontaneous smile to emerge from within.

Energy & Consciousness *Tiger, tiger, burning bright—As you allow yourself to get into your animal-like body and mind, let yourself feel what it is like to growl and snarl, and to embody the powerful strength of the graceful tiger. Were you able to let go of your "business as usual" state and become "animal-like"? Notice your energy and how you are feeling. As you soften and return to your initial position, how do you feel about the two different states?*

1 Stand or sit in a comfortable position.

2 Breathe naturally.

3 Warm up the jaw by bringing the lower jaw forward slowly. Try not to move the entire head forward when performing this exercise.

4 Repeat 3 times.

5 On the 4th time, let out a "Ha" sound as the lower jaw is thrust forward.

6 Feel the stretching of the Sternocleidomastoid muscle.

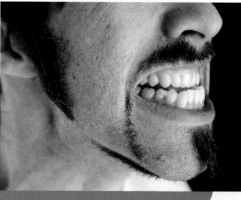

7 Repeat the thrust forward 3 times.

8 Now attempt to bite with the lower jaw thrust forward.

9 Repeat 3 times.

10 Note: As you thrust the jaw forward, your ears may pop and/or you may hear an unusual sound. This is natural, nothing to worry about.

11 Variation: If you would like, instead of letting out a "Ha" sound, try letting out angry, aggressive sounds. You can posture your body as if to attack with hands shaped into claws, your lower jaw forward striking out to bite an attacker. This will increase the intensity of the movement as well as bring forth emotional content as you perform the exercise.

Energy & Consciousness *While doing the variation, try to come in contact with the animal part of you. We all have this. Some of us call it our Lower Self, and it is capable of growling, hissing and snarling. Allow yourself the freedom to try this. If you won't allow yourself to do this, ask yourself, why not?*

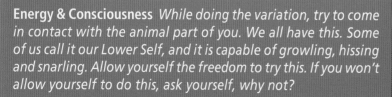

1 Stand or sit in a comfortable position.

2 Make fists with both hands.

3 Place the knuckles of both hands on either side of the lower jaw.

4 Massage outside rim of the jaw with knuckles at teeth level.

5 Begin at the tip of the chin and work toward the head.

6 Continue massaging and bring knuckles up toward the ear lobes and massage around the cheek bones.

7 Breathe.

8 With thumbs, gently massage under the jaw rim, beginning at ear level and returning to the chin.

9 Breathe continuously.

  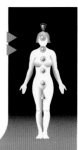

Energy & Consciousness *We hold a lot of emotions from early childhood in this area. The lower jaw muscles get activated as the baby begins to suck. The jaw is where we find blocked energy. The words that often come out are, "NO," or "I won't." Or is it sadness that you feel? Allow yourself a moment to get in touch with your feelings. What is your experience with this exercise?*

1 Stand or sit comfortably.

2 With your eyes closed, bring your attention to your face.

3 Notice any points of tension, numbness or just a "normal" feeling on face, mouth and throat.

4 Breathe deeply 3 or 4 times.

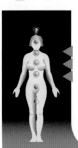

5 Slowly begin to purse your lips forward. As you do that, sound out the letter "U." This will help your lips to stretch forward as much as possible, creating a long sound conduit or what we recognize sometimes as a pout.

6 Sound out the letter "U" for a few seconds.

7 Now gradually begin to sound out the letter "E." Sounding out the letter "E" will naturally invite your lips to move from a pursed position to a wide-open, forced smile position.

8 Once you have reached sounding out the letter "E," sound the letter for a few seconds.

9 Now play with the sounding out of both letters "E" and "U." As you do this, your lips will move forward to a pout and then to a forced smile position.

10 Enjoy the stretching and the music that you are creating. Play with the pitch, intensity. Be goofy.

11 Slowly return to a comfortable facial expression.

12 Repeat 2 or 3 times.

13 How do your face, mouth and throat feel now? Do you feel like singing?

Energy & Consciousness *Are your jaw and lip muscles relaxed and do they move easily or are they tense and tight? Are you holding in some words, a shout or a scream? Are you able to relax? In moving your face muscles from a pout to a smile, does it change how you are feeling? As we move with this exercise, it becomes clearer and clearer how our body's posture can and does influence our mood and vice versa.*

1 *Wash your hands* before initiating this exercise.

2 Stand or sit in a comfortable position.

3 Place the Venus Mount—the soft padded area between your thumb and wrist—of your RIGHT or LEFT hand into your mouth.

4 Begin to suck, nibble and bite.

5 Experiment varying the intensity of the sucking, nibbling and biting.

6 Breathe naturally.

7 Spend as much time and repeat as often as you would like this exercise.

8 Note: Notice your feelings throughout this exercise. Did they change from the time you placed your hand into your mouth to the time you took it away? *Did it go from initial awkwardness and repulsion, to this feels good, to this is very soothing, to I like it?*

Energy & Consciousness *This helps to open the fifth chakra, which we use to affirm ourselves and speak our truth. It can also be very comforting and help us relax. This is what we did as infants and how we derived comfort and being fulfilled. We encourage you to do this exercise when you feel needy.*

8. Eyes & Head

Our eyes and head hold an enormous amount of tension. Noting the number of people who wear glasses or contacts, we can say without consulting an ophthalmologist that more than half of them do so because of muscles in stress. At the same time, we don't need to ask a neurologist to know that headaches plague millions of people every day. Again, stress is a major factor. Massage is a wonderful way to relieve stress, and in the exercises that follow, you can experience this by learning ways to massage and also to stimulate and release the accumulated stress from your eyes and your head. Give yourself a gift. You deserve it.

TEMPLE MASSAGE
INNER EYE BODY SCAN
EYE TENSION RELEASE
SCALP STIMULATION
MIRRORING
WIDENING RANGE OF VISION
THE BOILED EGG

91

1 Choose a comfortable standing or seated position.

2 Breathe deeply a few times.

3 Relax the shoulders.

4 Place your thumbs on your temples. Begin massaging the temples while breathing deeply.

5 Continue massaging, moving above the ears toward the back of the head and reaching the occipitals.

6 Breathe.

7 Move down toward the back rim of your skull; tip the chin forward for a better positioning of the hands and fingers and massage the rim of the skull with your thumb pads.

8 Breathe naturally and continuously.

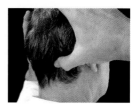

9 Now move down your neck and massage, either side of your neck with your knuckles.

10 Breathe deeply 4 times.

11 Relax the head and feel the energy begin to flow.

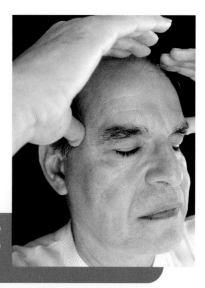

Energy & Consciousness *This comes under the heading of self care. There are many simple things we can do to make ourselves feel good. Think, I am taking care of myself because I deserve good care.*

1 Choose a comfortable standing, sitting or laying down position.

2 Take 5 deep breaths.

3 With each breath imagine the tension in your body being released into the ground.

4 Relax.

5 With your mind's eye, scan your body from head to toe.

6 Notice your impressions. What are the parts of your body you feel most comfortable with? Less comfortable? What are the parts you ignore or wish were not there?

7 Begin to seek your body's genetic, biological roots. How does my body express these roots? Where do I see my mother in my body? Where is my father? (Include other influences such as grandparents, siblings etc.) How do you carry these influences in your body, heart and mind?

8 Breathe deeply.

9 Place your RIGHT hand on your heart and do *The Pulsation of Your Being* in the Chest Energetic Exercise Section of this book.

10 Complete this exercise by taking 5 deep breaths.

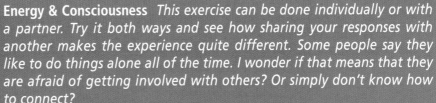

Energy & Consciousness *This exercise can be done individually or with a partner. Try it both ways and see how sharing your responses with another makes the experience quite different. Some people say they like to do things alone all of the time. I wonder if that means that they are afraid of getting involved with others? Or simply don't know how to connect?*

1 Choose a comfortable standing or seated position.

2 Breathe naturally.

3 Bring attention to eyes.

4 Place the tip of the thumbs on the inner rim of the eye socket below the eyebrow—this area is the up right and left hand corner of the eye socket, by the bridge of the nose.

5 Firmly press while breathing.

6 Release.

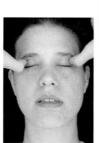

7 Press again.

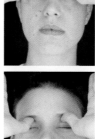

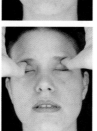

8 Repeat as many times as you would like.

9 Now press while contouring the ocular bone that runs parallel to the eyebrow.

10 Continuously breathe from the belly.

11 As you finish contouring the ocular bone, breathe 2 or 3 times and relax.

Energy & Consciousness *Often we do not even know that we are experiencing tension. It just accumulates little by little, and we adapt to it. It is only when we consciously relax that we can feel the tension leaving our body. You can do this exercise any time you choose throughout your day.*

1 Choose a comfortable standing or seated position.

2 With the finger pads, slowly massage the scalp, starting from the frontal lobes toward the back of the neck.

3 Enjoy.

4 Now back to the frontal lobes, with your fingers, start to gently pull the hair at the root so to stimulate the hair follicles.

5 Go around the entire head with both hands simultaneously massaging and gently pulling the scalp and hair.

6 To complete the massage, vigorously run your fingers randomly through your hair, as if washing it.

Energy & Consciousness *How does the energy feel now? You might feel a tingling or stimulating flow of energy. This short massage can move things when you get stuck. It can free you up and help you relax. It can bring more clarity to your thinking.*

1 Stand facing your partner.

2 Feet are parallel to each other, with feet shoulder-width apart. Knees are slightly bent. Hips are comfortably supported by legs. Abdomen is relaxed, as is the rest of the upper body. Face is naturally facing forward.

3 Place the palms of your hands against your partner's at chest height.

4 Keep eye contact with your partner and maintain a continuous and natural breathing rhythm throughout the exercise.

5 Choose who will lead the exercise first. The person chosen will be PARTNER A. PARTNER B will follow PARTNER A.

6 PARTNER A begins by moving slowly while PARTNER B mirrors by imitating the moves.

7 PARTNER A moves initially in a simple manner to become gradually more creative and elaborate. Maintain a slow pace so that PARTNER B can follow.

8 PARTNER A leads the movements for 3 minutes.

9 Switch.

10 PARTNER B moves slowly while PARTNER A mirrors by imitating the moves.

11 PARTNER B moves initially in a simple manner to become gradually more creative and elaborate. Maintain a slow pace so that PARTNER A can follow.

12 PARTNER B leads the movements for 3 minutes.

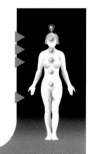

13 When you feel the exercise has become too easy, attempt to follow your partner with your eyes closed.

Energy & Consciousness *You might discover that you can follow energy with your eyes closed and you can sense energy. Wonderful. How can you use that ability? What might this door open in your life?*

1 Choose a comfortable standing or seated position.

2 Bring attention to eyes.

3 Firmly shut both eyes.

4 Hold breath and eyes shut for a few seconds.

5 Gradually open eyes and release the breathing.

6 Repeat 3 or 4 times.

7 Upper body facing forward and steady, slowly move eyes to the RIGHT side, as far to the side as possible, without moving the upper body.

8 Continue to breathe normally.

9 Hold eyes in the extreme position for 10 seconds.

10 Gradually return to forward-looking position.

11 Take 2 deep breaths.

12 Keep upper body, shoulder and abdomen as relaxed as possible throughout movement.

13 Repeat eye movement to the LEFT side.

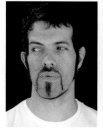
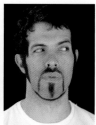

14 Looking forward, gradually direct eyes up toward ceiling. Roll eyes as far back and inward as possible.

15 Hold eyes in the extreme position for 10 seconds.

16 Return to forward-looking position.

17 Direct eyes down toward the floor and then inward.

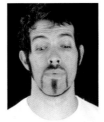 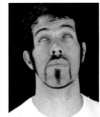

18 Hold eyes in the extreme position for 10 seconds.

19 Repeat this series 2 or 3 times.

20 Take 2 deep breaths. How is your vision now?

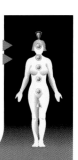

Energy & Consciousness *This exercise relaxes the eyes and releases accumulated strain. The human range of vision is 160 to 180 degrees, including peripheral vision. How much of this range are we really using? How much of what is happening around us are we not even aware of, let alone taking in? This exercise will bring more energy into this segment, which is also the reasoning center. Perhaps it will stimulate greater mental clarity.*

1 Standing or sitting comfortably, focus your attention on your eyes.

2 Rub the palms of your hands together until warm.

3 Place palms on both eyes while closed.

4 Let the warmth relax your eyes.

5 In a clockwise direction slowly massage your eye globe with your index finger.

6 Allow the massage to melt any tension so that the globe of the eye doesn't feel like a hardened egg.

7 Slowly massage one eye at a time.

8 Once again, place warm palms on both eyes.

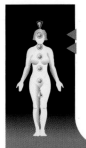

9 Note: Massage your eyes 2 to 3 times throughout the day while maintaining a natural breathing rhythm.

Energy & Consciousness *This massage decreases the accumulated tension of the optical globe by softening and relaxing it. The eye muscles become frozen, because we have the tendency to use the eyes not as a receptive organ but an organ that attacks. The eyes are said to be the doorway to our soul. Are we letting anyone see our soul? Or are we shutting them out? By softening the eyes, we are increasing our perception. How does that feel to you?*

9. Full Body

You have done the Energetic Movements for different body segments. Now you have the opportunity to experience the following exercises that will more fully integrate your whole body. You even have the chance to share these exercises with others and experience this as a group, if you choose. Many of these exercises will bring forth your exuberance, as well as your softness and gentleness. Be open to discovering more of who you are.

BALANCE
BODY TENSE-RELEASE
BODY ROLL
TEMPER TANTRUM
MODIFIED TEMPER TANTRUM
MEDITATION ON A LOVED ONE
THE NUMBER EIGHT
SHAKING ALL AROUND
FULL-BODY EXPLOSION
THE NOURISHING TOUCH
TUNING IN—BACK 2 BACK
JOY ROOM

1 Stand with feet spread apart at a comfortable distance. Feet are parallel to each other.

2 Knees are slightly bent. Hips are being comfortably supported by legs. The abdomen is relaxed, as is the rest of the upper body.

3 The head is naturally facing forward.

4 Arms are relaxed on either side of the body.

5 Stretch RIGHT arm in front of body, arm parallel to the floor. Palm is facing the floor.

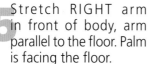

6 Slowly raise the LEFT leg as high as possible. Keep LEFT leg straight.

7 The LEFT arm stays to the side.

8 Keep eyes focused on the back of your RIGHT hand.

9 Stay in this position, while breathing normally, for a count of 10.

10 Switch legs.

11 Stretch LEFT arm in front of body while raising RIGHT leg as high as possible.

12 Keep eyes focused on the back of your LEFT hand.

13 Repeat the sequence 2 or 3 times.

14 Notice how your balance will improve as you repeat this exercise.

Energy & Consciousness *Our balancing system is important for any number of reasons that have to do with our health and over all well-being. Honing and refining this system goes a long way to keeping us healthy. Our body sends us messages when we are out of balance. If we are sensitive to these messages, we can respond to them. If we ignore or do not sense that a message is being sent, the cost to our health and state of well-being can be high. Let us seek to be balanced in our daily lives.*

1 Lay down comfortably on the floor.

2 Breathe deeply 3 times.

3 Relax your body.

4 Quickly tense your entire body, contracting: soles of the feet, toes, ankles, calves, knees, thighs, pelvis, buttocks, belly and its organs, diaphragm, chest, heart, arms, hands, shoulders, neck, throat, mouth, teeth, tongue, nostrils, face, eyes, head and even your thoughts.

5 Hold your breath.

6 Hold until you have reached *The Saturation Point*.

7 Release.

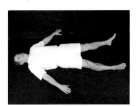

8 Relax all muscles simultaneously and let out a breath with a resounding "Ha."

9 Relax in this position for 2 to 4 minutes.

10 Repeat.

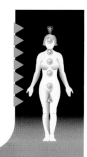

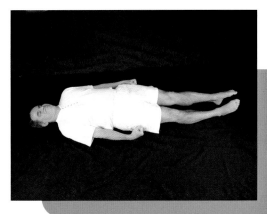

Energy & Consciousness *This is what it is like when we unconsciously bring tension into our body even though we do this little by little. Now we can feel how it is if we do this consciously. Do you like the way it feels? If not, notice when you are tense and purposefully relax your body. This way you have a choice as to whether you want to let it go or to keep it.*

1 You will need clear space on floor to be able to do this exercise.

2 Lay on the floor, belly up, and arms straight on either side of your head.

3 Breathe naturally throughout this exercise.

4 Begin to roll.

5 Roll slowly. Roll faster.

6 Roll for a few times in either RIGHT OR LEFT direction.

7 Let breath, giggles and tears flow.

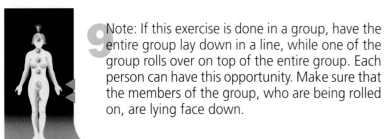

8 Enjoy the sensation of body in contact with the ground.

9 Note: If this exercise is done in a group, have the entire group lay down in a line, while one of the group rolls over on top of the entire group. Each person can have this opportunity. Make sure that the members of the group, who are being rolled on, are lying face down.

Energy & Consciousness *This is an opportunity to feel various parts of your body making contact with the ground in a playful manner. It is also an opportunity to just let go and let the momentum carry you, turning you round and round. Call out your inner child and invite her to come out and play.*

1 Stand with feet shoulder-width apart. Feet are parallel to each other.

2 Knees are slightly bent. Hips are comfortably supported by legs.

3 Abdomen is relaxed, as is the rest of the upper body.

4 Face is naturally facing forward. Eyes are closed.

5 Begin by alternating rising and stomping the RIGHT and LEFT heels to the ground.

6 Increase the speed and intensity

7 Include the arms.

8 Head is shaking from side to side as if saying NO.

9 Stop when you feel you can no longer maintain the *Temper Tantrum*.

10 Stand on feet, knees bent

11 Allow the body to vibrate up and down.

12 Arms are at your sides.

13 Breathe naturally. On the exhale, let out a sigh.

14 Gradually open eyes.

15 Note: This movement can also be done in a laying down position. Laying down on a mattress, the heels, arms and hands in fists will rhythmically hit against the mattress, while the head moves vehemently from side to side.

Energy & Consciousness *Once we realize that we can say "NO," we realize that we can also say "YES." It is that simple. Often energetically saying No allows the energy to dissipate, and a Yes is just around the corner. We find that life is not so much a matter of black and white, as it is different shades of the rainbow.*

1 You will need a cushion that fits on your lap for this exercise.

2 Sit comfortably with a cushion on your lap.

3 Feet are close together placed on the ground.

4 Take a few deep breaths.

5 Let out a sigh as you exhale.

6 Make fists with your hands.

7 Slowly begin to punch the cushion on lap.

8 While punching the cushion, include the stomping of feet on the ground.

9 As you stomp, let out a "Ha" sound.

10 Increase the speed and intensity of the punching.

11 Slowly return to your initial seated position.

12 Breathe deeply, letting out a sigh.

13 Lie down for 2 minutes and let your body relax.

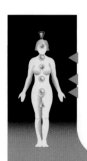

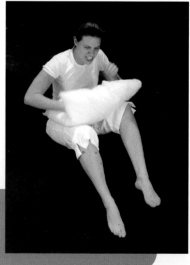

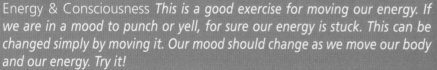

Energy & Consciousness *This is a good exercise for moving our energy. If we are in a mood to punch or yell, for sure our energy is stuck. This can be changed simply by moving it. Our mood should change as we move our body and our energy. Try it!*

1 Choose a comfortable standing or sitting position.

2 Close your eyes.

3 Breathe serenely.

4 Place your right hand over your heart.

5 Tune in to your heartbeat.

6 Breathe.

7 Smile, for you are present and have love in your heart.

8 Begin to invite the presence of your Loved One into your mind, heart, body and surrounding energy.

9 Feel your Loved One in your heart.

10 There is warmth, fire, beauty and deep joy filling the silence.

11 The whole universe is in front of you.

12 Notice your body.

13 Where do you feel your Loved One besides in your brain? Do you feel your Loved One in your chest? Stomach, pelvis, where? How does it feel?

14 Experience the presence of your love in your heart and how you experience your Loved One.

15 Meditate and send your Loved One all of the thoughts and feelings you have for you can reach his heart with this meditation.

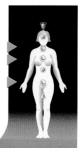

Energy & Consciousness *Can you let go of your inhibitions and get into doing this exercise? Try really flowing with the words. Feel the softness. You need a vivid imagination and a belief that this can be real. At the same time, you are doing this with your feeling center and not your mind. How do you feel? Do you sense any new possibilities for yourself?*

1 Stand with feet shoulder-width apart. Feet are parallel to each other.

2 Knees are slightly bent. Hips are comfortably supported by legs.

3 Abdomen is relaxed, as is the rest of the upper body.

4 Face is naturally facing forward.

5 Eyes are gently and pleasurably closed.

6 Breathe naturally and continuously throughout this movement.

7 Rub hands together until warm.

8 Set warm widespread palms on forehead.

9 Slowly move hands in a fluid and caressing touch down the front of the body.

10 Begin moving down the forehead, ears, eyes, nose, mouth, neck, shoulders, chest, rib cage, abdomen, pelvis, thighs, knees, shins, ankles, front of the feet and toes.

11 With the same slow, fluid and caressing touch, continue from the toes and go up the body, starting from the heels, calves, back of knees and thighs and buttocks.

12 Reach as far around and up your back as you can.

13 Move palms around to the belly and up the chest, rib cage and shoulders.

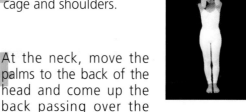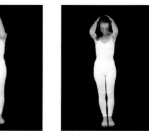

14 At the neck, move the palms to the back of the head and come up the back passing over the crown of the head.

15 Let arms and hands rest beside the body.

16 Take 5 deep breaths.

17 Stand still and savor the pulsation of life in the body.

18 Open eyes gently. Welcome to life.

19 Note: If you have difficulty reaching your feet, bend a little further at your knees. At the end you may gently caress your arms.

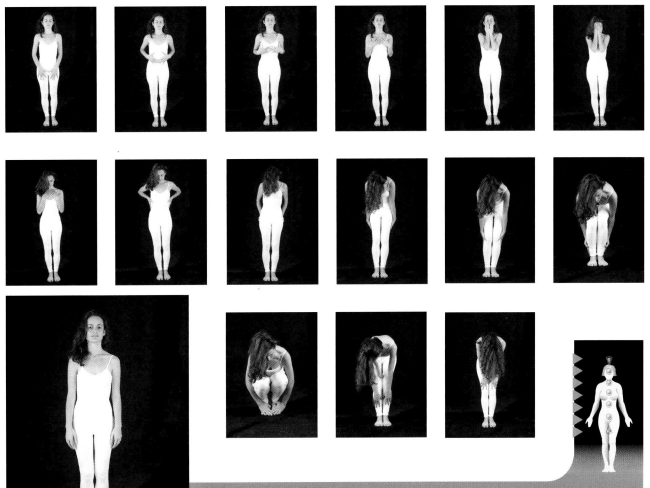

Energy & Consciousness *As you do the Figure Eight movements with your hands moving over your body, you will perceive that there is no end to this figure. The beginning of one part merges into the next figure eight. It is like the symbol of eternity. Try it.*

109

1 In standing position, begin to shake your body.

2 Let your whole body become limp as it shakes to the ground.

3 The head is relaxed, facing downward.

4 Breathe joyfully.

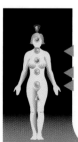

5 As you shake toes, feet, ankles, legs, pelvis, chest, arms, shoulders, neck, head and mouth, release the voice in a continuous "Ha" sound.

6 Open the chest and allow the breathing to come from the belly.

7 As you shake, think and express to those around you *"I want life!," "I want contact," "I want to open myself, to feel and allow what's in me to flow and become aware," "I choose to share myself."*

8 After shaking, slowly lie down or remain standing, knees slightly bent as body naturally vibrates.

9 Breathe deeply and feel the pleasure that is flooding your body.

10 This is a state of YES to LIFE!

11 Smile and Vibrate!

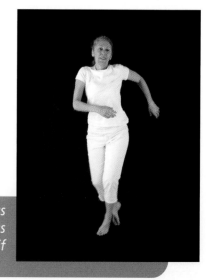

Energy & Consciousness *When we energize our whole body, this helps us say: Yes. Yes to life. The waves of energy that flow through and around us can move the sadness or negativity and allow for something new to enter, if this is what you want.*

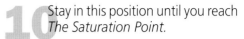

  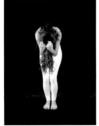 

1 Stand with feet shoulder-width apart. Feet are parallel to each other.

2 Knees are slightly bent. Hips are comfortably supported by legs.

3 Abdomen is relaxed, as is the rest of the upper body.

4 Face is naturally facing forward.

5 Arms are raised up toward the ceiling.

6 Eyes are closed.

7 Take 3 deep breaths.

8 Hold breath and tense every muscle from the top of the head to toes.

9 As body tenses up, body folds in contracted state into fetal position, head and arms tucked in, while still standing with knees bent.

10 Stay in this position until you reach *The Saturation Point*.

11 At this point, explode.

12 Move arms and legs outward into standing position.

13 Chest thrusts forward, head upward.

14 Eyes are wide open.

15 Release breath with ONE intense and open "Ha" sound.

16 Feel the vibration and expansion of the body and the release of tension.

17 Enjoy the freedom of brief weightlessness.

18 Return to initial standing position.

19 Repeat 2 or 3 times.

Energy & Consciousness *This exercise will energize your whole body. It will also give you the opportunity to consciously increase your tension-holding capacity. Your tension will be high, but you are in control of it. If you can control your tension when it is high, you can choose to let it go, explode and relax. It is a very empowering exercise. Usually when we explode in rage, it comes about automatically. Here we have the opportunity to do this movement intentionally and consciously. Can you see how increasing your tension tolerance and allowing yourself to discharge the tension can be useful in your daily interactions?*

1 Choose a comfortable standing or sitting position.

2 Place your RIGHT palm on your LEFT hand.

3 Touch your LEFT hand softly and slowly.

4 Put your consciousness and energy in every place that your hand touches.

5 Move your RIGHT palm up the LEFT hand.

6 Rest at several places as you travel up the LEFT arm and over the chest.

7 Caress the skin, as your RIGHT hand moves along.

8 Switch.

9 LEFT palm goes down the right arm.

10 Repeat this movement 3 or 4 times on each arm.

11 Feel this part of your body being energized and nourished.

When we focus our attention on something, we bring consciousness and energy into it. These elements bring the object of our attention to life. This goes for our left arm, any other part of our body, and even our feelings, thoughts, longings and personal goals.

1 Choose a comfortable standing or seated position.

2 Feel how you are in your body.

3 How is your energy flowing?

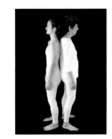

4 Once you have established an awareness of you in your body, approach your partner.

5 Stand or sit back to back, feeling yourself and then tuning in to your partner.

6 Breathe and take in your partner's presence.

7 Gradually move away

8 Check to see whether you can feel and keep the contact with yourself as well as with your exercise partner.

9 Note: You may choose to connect to your partner in such a way as to attempt to tune into her feelings and thoughts. See what comes up for you around what your partner may be feeling and thinking. At the end of *Tuning In—Back 2 Back,* both of you can share and compare notes on what you have picked up from one another.

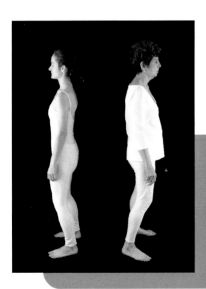

Energy & Consciousness *This is a simple opportunity to get in touch with yourself, make contact with another person and experience separateness while connected. Or said another way, to be aware of your energetic system when you are alone and when you are with another and then move into being alone once again. In one way or another, we do this many times in life. Will you permit yourself to do this now? Is your awareness of your physical and energetic body expanding?*

1 Invite the group to spread comfortably around the room.

2 The group is invited and encouraged to connect to, bring forth and express with their bodies their full capacity for joy and pleasure into the room.

3 Ask the group: *What would the expression of your joy look like?*

4 Let the individuals express themselves as long and as creatively as they wish.

5 Stimulate them to explore their outer space, body and people as well as their inner space of thoughts, images and emotions.

6 How much pleasure can we handle? Are we allowing ourselves to fully express our deepest and greatest delight?

7 What happens after we have *"reached the bottom of our well of pleasure"*? Where do we go from there?

8 Notice what happens to your body, mind and emotions. What do you feel like doing now after you have found your way of expressing your full capacity for joy and pleasure?

9 Share in pairs and later with the larger group.

10 Note: You may choose to play some background music during this exploration.

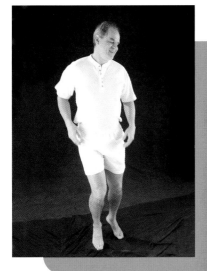

Energy & Consciousness *After this exercise you may begin to feel self-conscious, and the joy that you were able to sustain for awhile begins to fade away. The smile may still be on your face, yet the joy that radiates from it is no longer present. With this realization, your body that was once open, free, energized, upbeat, may now begin to contract. Your thoughts start to focus inward and feelings of sadness, tears and longing may emerge. Stay with your feelings, thoughts and longing. The natural cycle of life includes the expansion that pleasure brings as well as the contraction for integration and deepening our contact with ourselves. This will provide the ground that enables us to sustain and share another expansion of pleasure and delight.*

Individual Sample Program
19 exercises

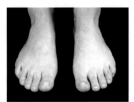

Toe Flexing
FEET & ANKLES
p. 11

Knee Warm-up
THIGHS & LEGS
p. 21

Weight Shift
FEET & ANKLES
p. 9

Body Drum
THIGHS & LEGS
p. 22

The Frog
PELVIS & ABDOMEN
p. 33

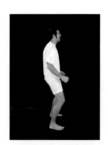

Standing Pelvic Thrust
PELVIS & ABDOMEN
p. 30

Get off My Back
CHEST
p. 43

Rib Cage Expansion
CHEST
p. 49

Heart above Head
CHEST
p. 46

Shoulder-to-Ear Stretch
ARMS & SHOULDERS
p. 63

Grounding Your Longing
ARMS & SHOULDERS
p. 69

Neck Rotations
NECK & THROAT
p. 74

The Lion
NECK & THROAT
p.72

Raisin & Olive Expressions
JAW & MOUTH
p. 84

Jaw Massage
JAW & MOUTH
p. 87

The Boiled Egg
EYES & HEAD
p. 100

Inner Eye Body Scan
EYES & HEAD
p. 93

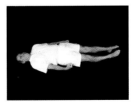

Body Tense-Release
FULL BODY
p. 103

The Number Eight
FULL BODY
p. 108

What Is Core Energetics?

Core Energetics—Origin and Perspective—Past and Present

Wilhelm Reich (1897–1957) was a disciple and member of Sigmund Freud's inner circle. Reich can be called the father of Energy Medicine. Two of Wilhelm Reich's most dedicated disciples were Dr. Alexander Lowen and Dr. John Pierrakos. They further developed methods of working with energy, blocks, breathing, and the body's armoring or defense system that is known today as Bioenergetics.

Lowen and Pierrakos also introduced a unique concept known as *grounding* to their body work. To be grounded means to stand consciously in a way that we can sense and feel our energy and our strength. To be grounded also means that we are able to support ourselves not only physically, but also in mind and spirit. This directs our awareness to the fact that we are connected to the earth, to the source of our energy as well as to Spirit; the source of our longing and fulfillment. I remember once in Dr. Pierrakos's class when he shared some of his experiences with us as a young medical student having recently come to New York from Greece. He credits the breathing exercises he learned from Reich, as well as the physical exercises to help ground him and to build up his energy system, with his success in medical school.

Some years later in his career as a psychiatrist, Dr. Pierrakos discovered the spiritual dimension to his work. He then founded the Institute of Core Energetics. The purpose of Core Energetics is to integrate body, mind, will and spirit. In this way, Core Energetics develops the capacity to love and to heal. The spiritual dimension comes from a body of knowledge that was given by Eva Broch Pierrakos in a series of lectures from 1957 to 1979, known as *The Pathwork*.

Core Energetics is an integrated approach to working with the growth and evolution of the whole person. It is body centered and connects energy and consciousness. The stream of our life energy comes from our Core, which is the essence of who we are. This energy flows in health and is blocked in disease. The blocks are disharmonious and cannot answer the needs of the organism. The work of the individual in Core Energetics is to become aware of our resistance to living life fully, and to be willing to release the energetic blocks. This is the purpose of the exercises in this book.

Thus, Core Energetics can be a deep and powerful therapeutic process. It teaches that the essence of life is love and pleasure. When negative energy, which is really distorted energy, such as fear or anger, is held in our physical and energy bodies, our physical and mental health may be threatened. The reason is that we hold, freeze or deny our feelings, which are then physically held in our body, in our tissues and in our cells. We do this by unconsciously contracting our muscles, which, in turn, increases tension by blocking feelings so that they cannot flow freely through the body. The release of such emotional blocks, defenses and belief systems through body work restores energy and consciousness to the individual. This release creates the possibility for greater life fulfillment.

Core Energetics also addresses the splits between the mind, heart and pelvis, which have to do with our sexuality. Done with consciousness, the exercises can provide a method of revealing to us our problems of intimacy and relationship, including addressing the enormous problem of sexuality that our society seems to be experiencing by separating our heart from our sexuality.

Dr. Pierrakos believed that modern medicine had forgotten the true source of health. In his search for this source, he discovered the vital energy of the Core, or the Essence that manifests in our body and in our life as pleasure, joy and love. It was from that place, the Core, that he passionately worked with his patients, trained therapists and lived his life.

Energy Anatomy

From a historical standpoint, the electromagnetic energy that surrounds the body and the chakra system have been known throughout many civilizations like Greece, Egypt and India for thousands of years. Some traditions name six chakras and many say there are seven major chakras. We are working with seven chakras in this manual. The chakras look much like spinning wheels. In the past, many healers and shamans could see them or sense them, but the ordinary person could not. There are healing schools today that teach their students ways to perceive, see and sense chakras. The chakras are important, because as each one spins, it generates energy that mixes with the energy generated by the other chakras to create the electromagnetic field, which is also called the aura. The openness and the amount of energy that is produced by the chakras have a direct relationship to our physical, mental and emotional health. For that reason, this system is extremely important.

We can say that each chakra has a point of view of its own, that is, each has a different way of energetically viewing reality. If we viewed reality from the first chakra, reality would be felt physically, from the second chakra's point of view; reality would be seen through an emotional setting. If we viewed reality through the third chakra, reality would be decidedly mental, which is the way most of the Western world actually sees reality.

The seven major chakras are located along a central axis parallel to the spinal column. Five of the seven chakras have a front and a back chakra. We can call A the front, and we can call B the back. The second through the sixth chakra connect with each other. There are also 21 minor chakras in the back and the front of the body.

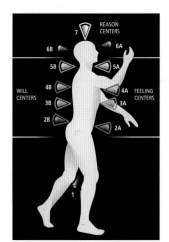

**Front & Back Chakras
and the Three Centers**

We can also look at the chakras from the standpoint of the following three centers: *Reason, Will* and *Emotion*. The front chakras comprise our Emotional center. The back chakras comprise our Will center, and the sixth chakra both A and B, front and back, and the seventh chakra constitute our Reason center.

Our chakras serve to vitalize our body. They interface with the vital life energy, and each operates in its own energetic reality in connection with the endocrine and nervous systems. In this way, they are directly involved in health as well as illness. One of the ways they keep us healthy is, when we do these exercises, we are energetically nourishing our glandular system. Each chakra nourishes a particular endocrine gland in our body, according to Barbara Brennan, author of *Hands of Light*. The first chakra nourishes the adrenals, the second chakra nourishes the gonads, the third the pancreas, the fourth the thymus, the fifth the thyroid, the sixth the pituitary and the seventh the pineal. Dr. Brennan further explains that the energy used by the chakras comes from what she calls Universal Energy. This energy is also known in the East as *Prana*, or *Chi.*

Since the Chakra system is not readily visible, most people do not know of it. It can be seen, however, by those who have the ability, or what is often called inner vision or second sight. The number of people who have this sight is growing more quickly than ever before, particularly among those who work with energy medicine. In the past, it was thought that one had to be born with this ability in order to have it. That is one way. However, it is possible to learn this as a result of practice, inner development and purification as well. Some people have their kinetic sense more highly developed than their visual sight, and that is why many people can sense the chakras without actually seeing them. Using their sense of touch, they can feel them. Dr. Brennan explained that in order to perceive the higher levels (chakras five, six and seven) she went into a meditative state with her eyes closed. Brennan's experience tells us that one of the ways that the higher chakras can be seen is with our "inner vision."

There are many systems that explain the location and the function of each chakra, and as one might expect, the information they give can be quite different, depending on the techniques used and the culture of the person who is working with chakras. Western cultures see the colors of the chakras one way and the Eastern cultures another way, according to Rosalyn Bruyere, author of *Wheels of Light*.

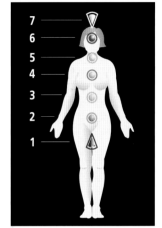

The Seven Major Chakras

The Chakra system used in this manual is the following: the first chakra which is below the genital area and between the legs, is called the Base chakra. The second chakra is just above the pubic arch and is called the Sacral Chakra. The third chakra is below the diaphragm, known as the solar plexus. The fourth chakra is at the heart. The fifth chakra is on the throat area, and the sixth chakra is the forehead with the seventh chakra known as the Crown Chakra. Little is known about the eighth and ninth chakras. The tenth chakra is of particular interest for our work in connecting physical movements and energy consciousness. According to Sharlene Young, an energy healer at the Rapid Eye Movement Institute in Oregon, the tenth chakra is below our feet and about a foot and a half below the ground. This chakra holds daily life energy and clarity about our life's purpose.

Gratitude

We would like to express our deep gratitude to *Andréa, Célia, Eduardo, Gus Alejandro, Mariela, and Vera* for being so willing to experiment, express themselves through these Energetic Movements and share the results with the readers of this book.

Thank you *Gastão Guedes* for the brilliant photography, design and layout. In addition, we would like to express our heartfelt thanks to *Studio Dialeto,* in São Paulo, Brazil, for allowing us to use their space for as long as we needed to complete the photo shoots and *Paul Shepard* for the many hours he spent editing the manuscript.

Alessandra would like to express her gratitude to Jalieh, who invited her to coauthor this book. Since both are Core Energetics therapists, their interests and passions are not far apart. As they are mother and daughter, she treasures this unique relationship that includes deep friendship, love and combining their individual learnings and gifts, to work and to serve. It is with great joy that she shares this labor of love with Jalieh.

Jalieh would like to thank all of the *graduates of the IV International Core Energetics Training* for the years they worked, explored, revealed, fought, loved and strengthened their bond with their deepest and most unique selves. Thank you for sharing those moments. Thank you for your transforming love.

Both Jalieh and Alessandra would like to openly and lovingly thank all the *teachers and colleagues* of the various trainings they have been involved with, who shared the exercises with them and inspired them to create new ones.

Collaborators' Notes

Andréa Castro Jota Teixeira has experience dancing, which she pursued starting at age 8 until she turned 23 years old. At age 14 she began teaching dance to children between 4 and 10 years of age. Andrea believes that using art is a way to enable the expression of each one of us as unique individuals. Presently, at age 25, Andrea studies psychology at the Paulista University and is involved in children's education. She has been developing a self-reflection teaching method for preschool children, which includes meditation and yoga. She has also participated in spiritual group work related to the White Brotherhood.

Célia Isabel Rodrigues, 54 years old, is a psychology graduate from the Catholic University in São Paulo. She is the founder and ex-director of the school Escola Espaço Aberto, de Educação Infantil also in São Paulo. She graduated from the UNIFMU teacher training program for Yoga Instructors. She presently offers Hatha yoga classes in her studio in São Paulo.

Eduardo Luiz Davidoff Chagas Cruz is 60 years old and works as a manager. He says, "The spirit navigates upon a body and forges on a process of continuous refinement. The body (psycho-physical) is the substrate of this spiritual existence. The spirit is plugged in the celestial web before, during and after this life. I believe in mysteries, and thus, in flexibility."

Gustavo Alejandro Rodriguez, who was born on October of 1969, is a physical education instructor, doing postgraduate studies in exercise physiology. "I have been teaching physical activities since 1993. I've been, in one way or another, practicing any type of physical activity for the past 35 years. I've done 6 years of Judo, 2 and half years of Wu-Shu (Kungfu), 8 years in a circus, 4 years of Spinning® and 20 years of dancing. All this workout taught me how to appreciate the subtleties of our body. Breathing is one of them, and it's an Art!"

Mariella Bondezan Afonso Rodriguez, who was born in July 1977, has a fashion design degree. "Art and body expression have great value in my personal and professional life. Being part of this project was a delicious trip to the center of my body, not only physical but Spiritual as well. Sharing this new and touching experience with very sensitive and touching people made it easier to open myself up to give the best of me for the success of this project."

Vera Dutra says, "To be involved with the work (modeling for this book) was a very sweet experience for me. One day I heard that people don't just cross our paths, they take a little bit of who we are and leave a little bit of who they are. Of the many gifts that I received from this work, one was to begin to perceive that we don't normally allow ourselves to breathe to our full potential. With that, we end up hindering ourselves from feeling great feelings such as the scent of things, places, people, the body's temperature, the scent of love, of a friend, the colors and the sounds of the world. Oxygen is life, it is peace, it is friendship, it is opportunity. So breathe deeply...breathe always...it is wonderful! A big kiss to all of you."

Bibliography & Further Readings

Baker, Elsworth F., M.D. – *Man in the Trap: The Causes of Blocked Sexual Energy.* Macmillan Publishing Company, 1967.

Black, Stuart – *A Way of Life: Core Energetics.* iUniverse, 2004.

Brennan, Barbara Ann – *Hands of Light: A Guide to Healing through the Human Energy Field.* Bantam Books, 1987.

Bruyere, Rosalyn L. – *Wheels of Light.* Edited by Jeanne Farrens, Simon & Shuster. Fireside, 1989.

Dychtwald, Ken – *Bodymind.* Jeremy P. Tarcher/Perigree Books, 1986.

Conger, John P. – *Jung & Reich: The Body as Shadow.* North Atlantic Books, 1988.

Keleman, Stanley – *The Human Ground: Sexuality, Self and Survival.* Center Press, 1976.

Johnson, Stephen M. – *Character Styles.* Norton & Company, 1994.

Judith, Anodea & Vega, Selene – *The Sevenfold Journey—Reclaiming Mind, Body & Spirit through the Chakras.* Crossing Press, 1993.

Lowen, Alexander – *Bioenergetics.* Penguin Group, 1975.

Lowen, Alexander – *The Betrayal of the Body.* Collier Books, MacMillan Publishing Company, 1967.

Nabb, Jerry – *Core Energetic Concepts of Grounding.* Southwest Center for Core Energetics. Self-published.

Pierrakos, John – *Core Energetics.* Life Rhythm Publication, 1987.

Pierrakos, John – *Eros, Love, & Sexuality.* Life Rhythm Publication, 1987.

Wilhelm, Reich – *Passion of Youth—An Autobiography, 1897-1922.* Edited by Mary Boyd Higgins and Chester M. Raphael, M.D. Paragon House, 1990.

About the Authors

Jalieh Milani completed her four-year training in Core Energetics in Germany with the founder of the discipline, Dr. John Pierrakos, and the International training director, Siegmar Gerken, Ph.D. She studied with Michael Mamas, founder and director of the School for Enlightenment and Healing in San Diego. There she deepened her knowledge of the body's energetic system and hands-on healing principles. She also graduated from Dartmouth College, majoring in economics. Since her childhood, Jalieh has shown interest and aptitude in using her body as an instrument for both self-knowledge and self-expression. At the age of 10, she became the State of São Paulo's Gymnastics Champion in Brazil. From that moment on, she began

to pursue a journey of exploring the body in sport, dance and theater. Jalieh has been working as a body therapist in Spain and Brazil for the past few years, offering workshops and trainings, assisting two Core Energetics specialization courses in Brasilia and São Paulo and seeing clients in her private practice. She presently lives in Durham, North Carolina, with her husband and two children, where she is a public speaker and offers seminars. Jalieh is a member of the Baha'i International Community.

Alessandra Shepard lived and worked in Brazil for 18 years. She holds a masters degree from Stanford University, and a Ph.D. in clinical psychology from the Catholic University in São Paulo. She cofounded one of the first Women's Crisis Centers in Brazil in the city of Campinas, and was a professor at the State University of São Paulo for 12 years. She maintained a private psychotherapy practice while living in Brazil. After leaving Brazil, she left her university position to pursue a career in energy medicine and body psychotherapy. She studied for four years at the world-famous Barbara Brennan School of Healing in the United States and another four years with the psychiatrist who created Core Energetics, Dr. John Pierrakos, and Siegmar Gerken, Ph.D. Alessandra has taught classes in various modes of awakening and given workshops in Spain, as well as the United States. She writes a column for a North Carolina magazine and is working on another book about energy and healing. Alessandra is currently living in Durham, North Carolina, with her husband, where she maintains a private practice, gives workshops and teaches.

How to contact the authors

Jalieh Juliet Milani

jaliehmilani@yahoo.com

Alessandra Shepard

alessandra@enocommons.org

Energetic Movement Index

Core Energetics in the World

Psychology as a field of human endeavor is growing and ascertaining that the ways that bring lasting health to individuals and organizations must address the human being as a whole. That is, health can only be sustained if the physical, emotional, mental and spiritual negations and aspirations of the individual are clearly and openly addressed. Presently Core Energetics can be sought and practiced in various centers in the United States and throughout the world. Below you will find contact information if you would like to further explore Core Energetics.

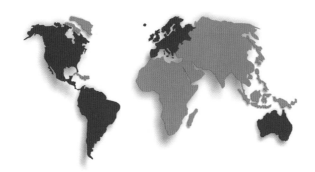

AUSTRALASIA

Australia
Australian Institute of Core Energetics
light@robertkirby.com
www.robertkirby.com

EUROPE

Germany
Institute of Core Energetics
Worldwide Trainings
Cornelia & Siegmar Gerken
Core@CoreEnergeticInstitute.com
www.CoreEnergeticsInstitute.com

Hedwig & Ruppert Lorusso
Teddy@core-energetics.de

Switzerland
Walid Daw
info@core-energetics.ch
www.core-energetics.ch

LATIN AMERICA

Brazil
Institute of Core Energetics—Brazil
Lucia Helena de Alencastro
lhdalencastro@hotmail.com

Monica Borine
inic.instituto@terra.com.br
www.inic.com.br

Ana Maria Gavazzi
anagav@uol.com.br

Mexico
Ilse Kretzschmar
Institute of Core Energetics
Calle Roberto Gayol No. 46
Col. Del Valle
Mexico D.F. 03100
info@yollocalli.com
www.yollocalli.com

NORTH AMERICA

California
Institute of Core Energetics
Worldwide Trainings
Cornelia & Siegmar Gerken
Core@CoreEnergeticInstitute.com
www.CoreEnergeticsInstitute.com

Georgia
Core Energetics Institute South
Pamela L. Chubbuck
coreenergetics@msn.com
www.core-energetics-south.com

New Mexico
Southwest Center for Core Energetics
Jerry Nabb & Irving Wahrhaftig
jlnabb@aol.com
irving@hubwest.com

New York
Institute of Core Energetics
coreeastinfo@aol.com
www.coreenergeticseast.org
1-800-901-1770

North Carolina
Jalieh Milani
Jaliehmilani@yahoo.com

Alessandra Shepard
alessandra@enocommons.org

Pennsylvania / Rhode Island
Midwest Institute of Core Energetics
Karyne B. Wilner
karynew@aol.com
www.coreenergeticseast.org

Northwest Pathwork and Core Energetics
Portland, OR
503-280-0880
nwpce@jps.net

The Pathwork of Self-Transformation
by Eva Pierrakos

"A useful trail guide for any individual who has chosen the path of genuine spiritual growth."
—D. Patrick Miller, *Yoga Journal*

A selection of the essential guided lectures given by Eva Pierrakos. Outlines the entire Pathwork process of spiritual development, including teachings on how to transform the negativity that blocks personal and spiritual evolution. A practical, rational, and honest way to reach our deepest creativity. Edited by Judith Saly.

Bantam, 1990.
ISBN 0-553-34896-5, 282 pgs, 5-1/8 x 8-1/4. U.S. $14.95

Fear No Evil
The Pathwork Method of Transforming the Lower Self
by Eva Pierrakos and Donovan Thesenga

"*Fear No Evil* can help us face our negative life experiences with a new light of understanding that will transform our personal pain into joy and pleasure."
—Barbara Brennan, author of *Hands of Light* and *Light Emerging*

Fear No Evil offers a practical method of compassionately observing and transforming our shadow side.

Pathwork Press, 1993.
ISBN 0-9614777-2-5, 296 pgs, 5-1/2 x 8-1/4 . U.S. $17.95

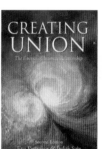

Creating Union
The Essence of Intimate Relationship
by Eva Pierrakos and Judith Saly

"A basic primer for all of us in relationship"
— Barbara Brennan, author of *Hands of Light*

Creating Union challenges us to courageously undertake the greatest adventure of life, the journey into fearless loving and self-realization with a kindred spirit. This book compassionately answers practical questions about love, sexuality and spirituality, divorce, fear of intimacy, creating mutuality, and how to keep the spark of eros alive.

Pathwork Press, 2002.
ISBN 0-9614777-8-4, 212 pgs, 5-1/2 x 8-1/4. U.S. $14.95

The Undefended Self
Living the Pathwork
Third Edition
by Susan Thesenga
based on material created by Eva Pierrakos

"A penetrating and highly effective guide in the psychological and spiritual search into the fundamental questions of life."
— *Leading Edge Review*

A profound and pragmatic guide to living the spiritual-psychological path (the Pathwork) to the undefended self, where we can no longer deny the presence of either evil or God within us. Includes true stories of people turning lifelong problems into occasions for positive movement and growth.

Pathwork Press, 2001
ISBN 0-9614777-7-6, 352 pgs, 6 x 9. U.S. $19.95

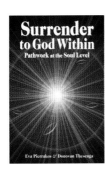

Surrender to God Within
Pathwork at the Soul Level
by Eva Pierrakos and Donovan Thesenga

"*Surrender to God Within* honors the absolutely essential step beyond an examined self
into a divinely directed life, and offers not only hope and promise but the path that can take you there."
— Pat Rodegast, author of the *Emmanuel* books

Takes us beyond personal growth into the deeper questions of life's meaning and reality.

Pathwork Press, 1997
ISBN 0-9614777-5-X, 216 pgs, 6 x 9
U.S. $14.95

Opening to Abundance
A 31-Day Process of Self-Discovery
by Charles Cresson Wood, based on material by Eva Pierrakos

"The promise upon which this work is built has been the Light that has lead me through the
last thirty years of my life. There are no words to express my gratitude. I unequivocally recommend
this work to every seeker of inner and outer truth."
— Pat Rodegast, author of the *Emmanuel* books

This serious exploration will give you tools to change your life for the better, presented in a workbook format, it will
teach you to bring willpower and discipline to manifest a new and abundant life.

Pathwork Press, 2004
ISBN 0-9614777-9-2, 158 pgs, 5-1/4 x 8-1/4
U.S. $11.95

Pathwork Press books, tapes, and CD can be purchased through your local bookstore,
through the Pathwork Press or through the Pathwork center nearest you.

Pathwork Press
P.O. Box 6010
Charlottesville, VA 22906
Phone (800) 728-4967; fax 434-817-2661
Email: pathworkpress@pathwork.org

Visit the Pathwork website at http://www.pathwork.org